Contents

© National Extension College Tru___ ___

DEVELOP YOUR MATHS

Develop Your Maths

Measures, Shape and Space

Level 1

NATIONAL
EXTENSION
COLLEGE

Measures, Shape and Space Level 1

© 2005 National Extension College Trust Ltd. All rights reserved.

ISBN 1 84308 315 9

Author:	Anne Rooney
Consultant:	Chrissie Minton
Project Manager:	Steve Attmore
Copy Editor:	Jean Twine
Proof-reader:	Andrew Johnston
Cover image:	GOODSHOOT/Alamy
Page design by:	John Matthews
Page layout by:	John and Deborah Matthews
Printed by:	Pear Tree Press Ltd

Every effort has been made to contact the copyright holders of material reproduced here.

The National Extension College is an educational trust and a registered charity with a distinguished body of Trustees. It is an independent, self-financing organisation. Since it was established in 1963 NEC has pioneered the development of flexible learning for adults. NEC is actively developing innovative materials and systems for open and distance learning opportunities on over 150 courses, from basic skills to degree and professional training.

For further details of NEC resources contact:

National Extension College Trust Ltd
The Michael Young Centre
Purbeck Road
Cambridge CB2 2HN

Tel 01223 400300 Fax 01223 400321
Email: resources@nec.ac.uk   website: http://www.nec.ac.uk

Registered charity 311454

Introduction

Welcome to the workbook on measures, shape and space. This workbook will help you to use and understand different ways of counting and measuring things, including:

- money

- time

- distance

- weight

- temperature

- area

- volume.

This workbook is part of NEC's 'Develop Your Maths' series. The series has been produced in response to a need for materials for Level 1 Numeracy.

The other parts of the series are:

- Number

- Handling data.

You must complete all three workbooks, or be confident in the skills covered, before taking the Numeracy Level 1 national test. You can find out more about this test in the section called 'Information on the National Test' at the back of the workbook.

In everyday life, we often need to be able to count or measure things. You might need to:

- work out how much things cost

- tell the time, and work out how long something will last

- compare the sizes of things you might want to buy

- work out how large a room is.

By helping you to understand how different things are measured and counted, this workbook will help you make sense of such tasks.

The national standards for adult numeracy

In Autumn 2000 the government launched a national strategy to improve the numeracy skills of adults in England. The strategy includes:

- national standards for adult numeracy

- a core curriculum to show what learners need to know in order to reach those standards

- a new system of qualifications in line with the standards

- better learning opportunities to meet the needs of a wide range of learners.

The standards describe adult numeracy as 'the ability… to use mathematics at a level necessary to function at work and in society in general'.

The standards provide a map of the range of skills that you are expected to need.

Numeracy covers the ability to:

- understand and use mathematical information

- calculate and manipulate mathematical information

- interpret results and communicate mathematical information.

Level 1 of the national adult numeracy standards is equivalent to Key Skills Level 1 and NVQ Level 1.

Aims of the workbook

The aims of the workbook are to provide:

- examples of numeracy from everyday life, with relevant methods shown

- lots of learning activities in different practical contexts.

By the time you have completed this workbook you will be able to:

- add, subtract, multiply and divide sums of money

- understand the time shown in different ways, and work out time intervals

- use common measurements for distance, weight, temperature and capacity

- measure and work out the perimeters and areas of flat shapes

- work out the volume of simple 3-D shapes.

Who the workbook is for

Over 7 million adults in England have difficulty with numeracy. This means they have difficulty doing tasks such as calculating how much change they should get or working out how to change a fraction to a decimal.

How to use the workbook

You have probably chosen this workbook because you, or a tutor, have identified the need for you to develop skills, knowledge and understanding of working with measures, shape and space.

This workbook is divided into five sections:

- Money

- Time

- Measuring

- Shapes

- Space.

Each section is divided into topics. Each topic begins with a short introduction, which puts the subject into context. Key terms are printed in bold. Definitions of these terms appear in the Glossary section at the end of the workbook.

The text is full of worked examples for you to follow. You can then put what you learn into practice by tackling the activities that follow the examples.

There are suggestions for answers to each of the activities. Always check them before going on to the next activity. You may need to cover up the answers while working on an activity.

If you find that you have made errors in the calculations, or have got several answers wrong, go back over the relevant material in the section before attempting to move on to the next topic.

> ### Hints/Tips
> Handy hints and useful tips are provided as aids to memory.

At the end of the section you may find a set of 'self-check' questions. These are designed to help you to check that you have understood the concepts covered in that section. Answers to the self-check are included at the end of the section.

Resources

For your work on this workbook you will need the following:

	Section 1	Section 2	Section 3	Section 4	Section 5	Assignments
Notepaper and pen/pencil	✔	✔	✔	✔	✔	
A calculator	✔					
A ruler			✔	✔		✔
A tape measure			✔	✔		
A pair of scissors				✔		
Printed bus and train timetables, or a computer connected to the Internet (not essential)		✔				
A set of scales			✔			
A thermometer			✔			
A measuring jug			✔			
Coloured card, or white card and coloured pens or pencils				✔		

Section 1: Money

Section 1: Money

In this section you will practise working with money. This will help you buy and sell things. It will also help you to manage your budget.

Reasons for completing this section

Thinking about the things in this section will enable you to:

- add up the cost of things you want to buy

- work out how much change to expect, or how much money you will have left after spending some or taking some away

- work out how much several items of the same price will cost

- divide up a bill or share an amount of money.

Resources

You will need a calculator for your work on Topic 2.

Topic 1: Adding and subtracting money

In this topic, you will find out how to add up amounts of money and how to subtract (take away) one amount of money from another.

Think of a situation in which you would need to be able to add up two or more amounts of money.

Curr. ref: MSS1/L1.1

When might you need to take one amount of money away from another?

You will need to **add up** money to:

● go shopping

● work out what a holiday or project will cost

● check a bill or credit card statement.

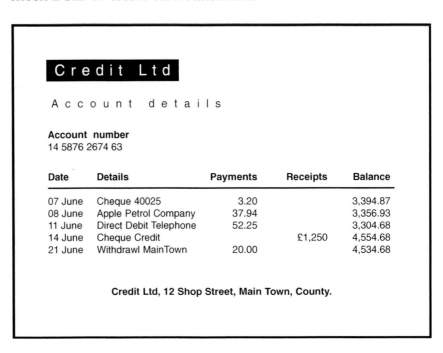

Credit Ltd

A c c o u n t   d e t a i l s

Account number
14 5876 2674 63

Date	Details	Payments	Receipts	Balance
07 June	Cheque 40025	3.20		3,394.87
08 June	Apple Petrol Company	37.94		3,356.93
11 June	Direct Debit Telephone	52.25		3,304.68
14 June	Cheque Credit		£1,250	4,554.68
21 June	Withdrawl MainTown	20.00		4,534.68

Credit Ltd, 12 Shop Street, Main Town, County.

You will need to **subtract** one amount of money from another to

● work out the change to expect or give when buying and selling things

● work out how much money you will have left if you buy something

● check the amount taken away for tax and other deductions on your pay slip.

There are lots of times when these skills are useful. You might have thought of different examples.

Adding amounts of money

When you add or subtract money, remember to write the numbers down so that the **decimal points** line up. If you don't do this, you might get the columns mixed up.

SuperMarket	
Baked Beans	£ 1.14
Yoghurts	£ 1.25
Milk	£ 1.04
Carrots	£ 0.59
Bread	£ 0.75
Toothpaste	£ 0.79
Toothpaste	£ 0.79
MultiSave Discount	£ 0.20 −
Cereal	£ 1.49
Biscuits	£ 0.69
Potatoes	£ 1.49
Crisp Multipack	£ 1.09
Total	£ 10.91
Visa Debit	£ 10.91

Thank you for shopping with us
Come again soon!!
15/12/2004 11:47

If you need to use a whole number of pounds, such as £3, write it like this:

£3.00

to help you keep the numbers in the right places.

Change numbers of pence to pounds. So write 15p as £0.15. Then you can line up numbers properly, like this:

$$£3.00$$
$$+ \underline{£0.15}$$
$$\underline{£3.15}$$

Look at this example to check you know how to add up amounts of money.

Example 1

You go on a trip by train. You have to pay 80p to park your car and £13.75 for your train ticket, then £2 for a bus. How much does the trip cost?

Travel Ticket UK

Anytown to City
leaving 08.00 arriving 08.55

City to Anytown
leaving 04.30 arriving 5.28

£13.75

Hint

Remember that 80p is the same as £0.80 and that £2 is the same as £2.00.

Method:

Change all the amounts to pounds and pence, and write the numbers down so that the decimal points line up, like this:

Parking, 80p	£0.80
Train ticket	£13.75
Bus, £2	£2.00
	£16.55

Now try these.

Activity 1

1   You buy three books from an online bookshop. The books cost £6.75, £11.99 and £5.50. How much will they cost all together?

If the books come to more than £20, delivery is free. Will you get free delivery?

2   You want to rent two videos and buy a packet of crisps. One is a children's video and costs £1.15 to rent. The other is an adult video and the rental is £3. The crisps cost 47p. How much do you need to spend?

3   You have been given this bill in a café. Is it correct?

Tea	1.20
Scone	1.10
Butter	0.35
Cream	0.85
Jam	0.65
	3.95

Check your answers with our suggestions before you carry on.

Suggestions for Activity 1

1   You need to work out

£6.75 + £11.99 + £5.50

and see whether the answer is more or less than £20.

$$£6.75$$
$$+ £11.99$$
$$\underline{+ £5.50}$$
$$\underline{£24.24}$$

The books cost more than £20, so delivery is free.

2 You need to work out

£1.15 + £3 + 47p

Write it like this:

$$£1.15$$
$$+ £3.00$$
$$\underline{+ £0.47}$$
$$\underline{£4.62}$$

Answer: £4.62

3 To check the bill you need to work out

£1.20 + £1.10 + 35p + 85p + 65p

$$£1.20$$
$$+ £1.10$$
$$+ £0.35$$
$$+ £0.85$$
$$\underline{+ £0.65}$$
$$\underline{£4.15}$$

So the bill is wrong.

Subtracting amounts of money

Remember to line up the numbers and convert them all to pounds and pence.

Example 2

You have £12.53 left in your pocket. You need to get the bus home, which will cost £1.70. You want to buy a magazine for £2.80, but you would also like a snack. How much can you afford to spend on the snack and still have enough for the magazine and the bus home?

Single
£1.70

Method:

You need to add up what you have to spend on the magazine and the bus fare and subtract the answer from £12.53.

£12.53 – (£1.70 + £2.80)

First, add together the cost of the magazine and the bus fare:

Magazine:	£2.80
Bus fare:	+ £1.70
	£4.50

Then take this away from £12.53:

£12.53
– £4.50
£8.03

Hint

If you have a sum in brackets, always do this first.

Now try these.

Activity 2

1   Your credit card bill says you owe £284.39. You have already paid £131.16, which isn't shown on the bill. How much more do you still have to pay?

2   You are helping out on a school trip. One child has £3 spending money. In the gift shop, the child wants to buy a pencil for 37p and a ruler for 99p. Will he have enough money left to buy a pack of stickers for £1.25?

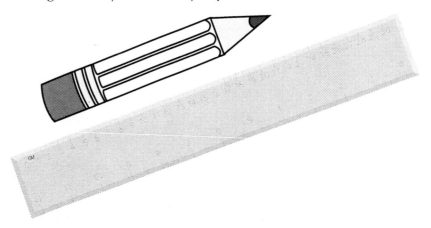

3   You are preparing a pay slip. How much money will this person get this week?

Gross pay	£370.60
Overtime	+ £79.75
Less tax	− £83.73

Check your answers with our suggestions before you carry on.

Suggestions for Activity 2

1   You need to work out

£284.39 − £131.16

£284.39

− £131.16

£153.23

2   You need to work out

£3 − (37p + 99p)

and find out whether the answer is £1.25 or more.

£3 − (37p + 99p)

£0.37

+ £0.99

£1.36

= £3 − £1.36

£3.00

− £1.36

£1.64

This is more than £1.25, so the child can afford stickers.

3   You need to work out

£370.60 + £79.75 − £83.73

£370.60

+ £79.75

£450.35

= £450.35 − £83.73

£450.35

− £83.73

£366.62

Summary

In this topic you have learned how to add up amounts of money and how to take one amount of money away from another.

> Topic 1 covers these parts of the Common Measures curriculum:
>
> ● 'write whole numbers and decimals'
>
> ● 'line up the decimal point when adding and subtracting amounts of money'.

Topic 2: Multiplying and dividing money

Curr. ref: MSS1/L1.1

In this topic, you will find out how to multiply and divide amounts of money.

You might want to multiply an amount of money if you were going to buy several items of the same price. This means you can find out how much they would cost all together.

Can you think of a time when you might need to divide an amount of money?

You might need to work out your part of a bill that was shared with other people, or you might need to work out how much money you have each week from a monthly budget.

There are lots of other times when these skills are useful. You might have thought of different examples.

Multiplying amounts of money

When you **multiply** with money, make sure you put the decimal point in the right place in your answer. There should always be two numbers after the decimal point, showing the number of pence.

Look at this example.

Example 3

You want to buy four small towels that cost £5.65 each and two large towels that cost £12.20 each. How much will they come to all together?

Method:

You need to work out (4 x £5.65) + (2 x £12.20). Work out the two multiplications first and then add the answers together.

You can forget about the decimal point for now, because you can put it back in at the end.

$$565$$
$$\underline{\times\ 4}$$
$$2260$$

Use the last two numbers for pence. The four small towels cost £22.60.

Now do the next sum:

$$1220$$
$$\underline{\times\ 2}$$
$$\underline{2440}$$

= £24.40 for the large towels.

The total price is

$$£22.60$$
$$+\ \underline{£24.40}$$
$$\underline{£47.00}$$

Hint

Do a rough calculation using whole numbers to help you check if your answer looks right: 4 x £5.65 will be between 4 x £5 and 4 x £6, so between £20 and £24.

Hint

Remember there will be two numbers after the decimal point, for the pence.

Now try these.

Activity 3

1   You want to buy a washing machine, paying for it over a year. There will be 12 payments of £37.60. How much will the washing machine cost? Use a calculator.

2   You are going to lay a patio. You need 90 paving stones that cost £4.50 each. How much will they cost all together?

Hint

Work out the total cost of a drink and a meal, then multiply by 4.

3   You are with three friends and you buy fish and chips and a drink. The meals cost £5.78 each and the drinks cost £1.20 each. How much will it cost for four meals and four drinks?

Check your answers with our suggestions before you carry on.

Suggestions for Activity 3

1   You need to work out

£12 × £37.60

Press these keys on your calculator:

$\boxed{1}\,\boxed{2}\,\boxed{\times}\,\boxed{3}\,\boxed{7}\,\boxed{\cdot}\,\boxed{6}\,\boxed{0}\,\boxed{=}$

The answer should be £451.20.

Do a rough check on your answer. As £37.60 is a bit less than £40, so your answer should be around 12 × £40 = £480.

2   You need to work out

90 × £4.50

450

× 90

40500

Put the decimal point back in:

£405.00 is the total cost of the paving slabs.

Do a rough check. If you bought 100 paving slabs for £4.50, the cost would be 100 × £4.50 = £450.

3   You need to work out

(£5.78 + £1.20) × 4

Each meal and drink cost

£5.78

+ £1.20

£6.98

Four meals with drinks cost

£6.98

× 4

£27.92

Do a rough check. £6.98 is nearly £7; 4 × £7 = £28.

Dividing or sharing amounts of money

You will need to **divide** amounts of money when you work out shares of a bill, or of prize money.

When you divide a sum of money, be careful about the decimal point. It will not always be the last two figures. Look at this:

£2.15 ÷ 2 = £1.075

There are three numbers after the decimal point. If you tried to use the last two for pence, the answer would come out as £10.75 – which is clearly wrong.

£1.075 is £1.07$\frac{1}{2}$p. We don't use a halfpenny any more, so you need to round this up to £1.08 or down to £1.07.

Always do a rough calculation to check your answer and show you where the decimal point should go.

Example 4

You live in a house with two friends. You share the electricity bill equally. The bill is for £63.75. How much do you each have to pay?

Method:

There are three of you, so you need to divide the bill by 3:

$$\frac{21.25}{3)\overline{63.75}}$$

If you used a calculator, you would press these buttons:

⑥ ③ · ⑦ ⑤ ÷ ③ =

You have to pay £21.25 each.

Now try these.

Activity 4

1   You have bought a retirement present for a work colleague. Six of you have agreed to split the price equally. The present cost £39. How much must you each pay?

2   You have bought 5 metres of curtain fabric for £67.50. You want to buy an extra metre to make a cushion cover. How much will it cost?

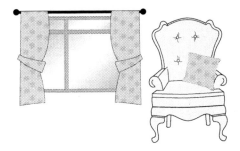

3   a)   You earn £1,260 a month. You can spend a quarter of this each week. How much do you have each week?

    b)   You have to pay £540 rent each month. How much do you have left from your £1,260?

    c)   How much do you have left each week, after paying the rent?

Check your answers with our suggestions before you carry on.

Suggestions for Activity 4

1   You need to work out

£39.00 ÷ 6

$$\begin{array}{r} 6.50 \\ 6\overline{)39.00} \end{array}$$

To check the answer, think through the six times table. If the present was £36, you would each pay £6. If it was £42, you would each pay £7.

2   You need to work out

£67.50 ÷ 5

$$\begin{array}{r} 13.50 \\ 5\overline{)67.50} \end{array}$$

So the fabric cost £13.50 per metre.

If you used a calculator, you should have pressed these buttons:

6 7 $\cdot$ 5 0 $\div$ 5 $=$

Check your answer. £67.50 is close to £60, and £60 ÷ 5 = £12.

3   a)   You need to work out

£1,260 ÷ 4

$$\begin{array}{r} 315 \\ 4\overline{)1260} \end{array}$$

You would have £315 for each week.

As a rough check, £1,200 ÷ 4 = £300.

b)   You need to work out

£1,260 – £540

$$\begin{array}{r} £1,260 \\ -\ \underline{£540} \\ \underline{£720} \end{array}$$

So you have £720 left for the month.

c) You need to work out

£720 ÷ 4

$$\begin{array}{r} 180 \\ 4\overline{)720} \end{array}$$

So you have £180 a week after paying rent.

As a rough check, £800 ÷ 4 = £200.

Summary

In this topic you have learned how to divide or share amounts of money and how to multiply with money.

Topic 2 covers these parts of the Common Measures curriculum:

● 'write whole numbers and decimals'

● 'line up the decimal point when adding and subtracting amounts of money'.

Section 2: Time

Section 2: Time

In this section you will practise working with clocks and time. This will help you to tell the time, to work out how long something will take and to use timetables.

Reasons for completing this section

Thinking about the things in this section will enable you to:

● understand times shown using the 12-hour clock and the 24-hour clock

● work out time intervals – such as how long it is between the start and end time of an event

● use timetables.

Resources

Access to a computer you can use to find timetables online will be useful for your work on Topic 3, but you will still be able to do Topic 3 if you do not have this.

Topic 1: Working with time

In this topic, you will find out about different units of **time** and learn to convert between them.

When might you need to work out how many minutes are in a period of time given in hours?

Curr. ref: MSS1/L1.1

When might you need to convert between days and weeks or months?

There are lots of occasions when these skills are useful. Some examples are:

● to work out how many hours of exercise you have done over a week, in bursts of 20 or 40 minutes

● to work out how much holiday you have taken or can take

● to work out how many hours and minutes a film lasts, when the length is given in minutes.

You might have thought of different examples.

Short times

Short periods of time are measured in seconds, minutes and hours.

60 seconds = 1 minute

60 minutes = 1 hour

To find out how many seconds are in a period shown as minutes, you need to **multiply** the number of minutes by 60. To find out how many minutes are in a period shown as seconds, you need to divide the number by 60. Converting between minutes and hours is just the same.

Usually, you will need to know the whole number of minutes (or hours) and the remainder in seconds (or minutes). This means your answer will be something like 'two minutes and twenty seconds'. If the remainder was 30 seconds you might say 'two and a half minutes' instead.

Example 1

A recipe says to beat the mixture for two and a half minutes. You don't have a timer, so decide to count seconds. How many should you count to?

Method:

To convert from minutes to seconds, you need to multiply by 60, so

$2\frac{1}{2} \times 60$

$= 120 + 30$

$= 150$ seconds.

Example 2

You have been training for a fun run and use a stop watch to time your running. The time it took you to run to the end of the road is 203 seconds. How many whole minutes and extra seconds did it take?

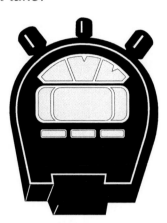

Method:

To convert from seconds to minutes, you need to divide by 60. Find the whole number of minutes – the whole number of 60s – and then show the remainder as seconds.

You need to work out 203 ÷ 60. This looks quite hard. But you can use the six times table to see how many seconds are in different numbers of minutes:

60 seconds = 1 minute

2 x 6 = 12, so 2 x 60 = 120 seconds = 2 minutes

3 x 6 = 18, so 3 x 60 = 180 seconds = 3 minutes

4 x 6 = 24, so 4 x 60 = 240 seconds = 4 minutes

203 falls between 180 and 240, so it's a bit more than 3 minutes. Now work out the remainder:

203 – 180 = 23 seconds

So the run took 3 minutes 23 seconds.

Now try these.

Activity 1

1   You are mending something and you need to leave the glue to set for 90 seconds. You have a timer that you can set in minutes and seconds. How should you set it?

2   You are childminding for a friend. You have told the son that he must go to bed in two hours. He wants to watch a video. The labels on his videos show the length of the film in minutes. How long, in minutes, is the longest video he can watch?

The film he wants to watch lasts 112 minutes. Does he have time to watch it? How many hours and minutes will it last?

3   You hire a boat on the river. The boat hire costs £15 an hour. You are on the river for 210 minutes. How many hours do you have to pay for?

Check your answers with our suggestions before you carry on.

Suggestions for Activity 1

1   You need to work out

   $90 \div 60 = 1$ minute 30 seconds, or $1\frac{1}{2}$ minutes.

2   The longest video he can watch is two hours, so you need to work out how many minutes this is:

   $60 \times 2 = 120$ minutes

   112 minutes is less than 120 minutes, so he can watch the video.

   $112 - 60 = 52$

   So the video will last 1 hour 52 minutes.

3   You need to work out how many hours and minutes are in 210 minutes.

   60 minutes = 1 hour

   120 minutes = 2 hours

   180 minutes = 3 hours

   240 minutes = 4 hours

   210 minutes is between 3 hours and 4 hours

   $210 \div 60 = 3$ hours remainder 30 minutes

   $210 - 180 = 30$ minutes

   You need to pay for 3 hours 30 minutes, or $3\frac{1}{2}$ hours.

Longer times

Longer periods of time are shown in days, weeks, months or years.

24 hours = 1 day

7 days = 1 week

The number of days in a month varies. It can be 28, 29, 30 or 31. People often count four weeks as a month, or count a month as 30 days. There are 12 months in a year.

Use this rhyme to help you remember how many days are in each month:

Thirty days have September,

April, June and November.

All the rest have thirty-one

Excepting February alone.

February has 28 days most years, and 29 in a leap year. Leap years come every four years (2004, 2008, 2012, etc).

To work out how many weeks are in a period of time shown as days, you need to divide the number by seven. To work out how many days are in a period shown as weeks, you need to multiply the number by seven.

Very long periods are shown in centuries or millennia.

100 years = **1 century**

1000 years = **1 millennium**

You might come across these if you watch a history programme, for example. You might hear something like 'the empire lasted for four centuries'. This means it lasted 400 years.

Example 3

a) You take out holiday insurance for 35 days. You want to go to France for four weeks. Does your insurance cover your trip?

b) You will travel around for 10 days and rent a house for the rest of the time. Fill in the rental form for the house.

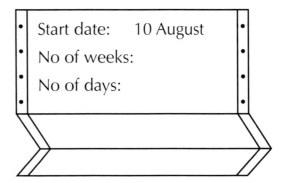

Start date: 10 August

No of weeks:

No of days:

Method:

Hint

If you have a sum in brackets, always do this first.

a) You need to work out the length of your trip in days. There are seven days in a week.

4 x 7 = 28

28 is a lower number than 35, so your insurance will cover your trip.

b) You are travelling for 10 days. You need to work out how many days are left, and change this number to weeks.

28 – 10 = 18 days

You need to rent the house for 18 days. Divide this number by seven to find out how many weeks it is:

18 ÷ 7 = 2 weeks 4 days

You need to rent the house for two weeks and four days.

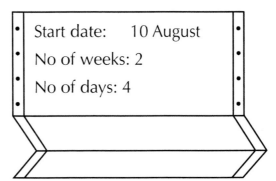

Start date: 10 August

No of weeks: 2

No of days: 4

Now try these.

Activity 2

1   A farmer has hatched some chicks. They need to be fed chick crumbs until they are seven weeks old. The chicks eat one bag of chick crumbs each day. How many bags does the farmer need to buy for each chick?

2   You have a packet of pills that contains 56 pills. You have to take one a day.

   a)   How many should you have taken after two weeks and four days?

   b)   How many more weeks and days must you take the pills for?

3   You have signed up for a free trial for an Internet connection. It runs for 60 days. How many weeks can you use the Internet for?

Check your answers with our suggestions before you carry on.

Suggestions for Activity 2

1   You need to work out

   7×7 days = 49 days

   So the farmer needs to buy 49 bags of food.

2   a)   You need to work out how many days are in two weeks and four days:

   $2 \times 7 = 14$ days in two weeks

   $14 + 4 = 18$ days.

b) You should have taken 18 pills. To find out how many more weeks and days you need to take the pills, work out how many days are left:

56 − 18 = 38

Then work out how many weeks and days this is:

38 ÷ 7 = 5 weeks 3 days

(5 × 7 = 35)

So you need to take the pills for another 5 weeks 3 days.

3 You need to work out

60 ÷ 7 = 8 weeks 4 days

(8 × 7 = 56)

So you can use the Internet for 8 weeks 4 days.

Summary

In this topic you have learned how to work with short and long periods of time.

Topic 1 helps you cover these parts of the Common Measures curriculum:

● 'know the units of time: millennium, century, year, month, week, day, hour, minute, second'

● 'know the relationship between units of time, e.g. 1 hour = 60 min'

● 'convert units of time, e.g. 70 minutes is 1 hour 10 minutes'.

Curr. ref: MSS1/L1.1

Topic 2: Using the clock

In this topic, you will find out how to use different types of clocks that show 12 hours and 24 hours.

Some clocks show the time in numbers, and others on a round face with hands. You need to be able to use both kinds.

Can you think of a place where you need to read the time from a **12-hour clock?**

Where or when do you need to understand the **24-hour clock?**

When do you need to convert between 12-hour times and 24-hour times?

You might use different types of clocks at home, or at home and work. For example, you might have a clock on the wall that shows the time on a clock face with 12 hours marked.

Many digital clocks use the 24-hour clock. Clock-radios, clocks in cars and in some public places such as railway stations often show a 24-hour clock.

You often need to convert between 12- and 24-hour times to use timetables or to set a clock on a computer or video recorder. You might have thought of different examples.

12-hour times and 24-hour times

A clock-face shows the time divided into 12 hours. It starts with both hands at the top at the beginning of the day, **midnight**:

At any point you can read the time by looking at the position of the hands.

At **midday** the hands are back at 12 o'clock and the clock starts again for the afternoon. You can't tell from a 12-hour clock whether it is morning or afternoon.

> **Tip**
> Midday is also called noon.

Digital clocks show the time as a display of numbers:

Some show 12-hour times. They might show 'am' or 'pm' beside the number so that you can see whether it's morning (am) or afternoon (pm).

Hint

Times can be shown as 07:00, 07.00 or 0700, or even as 7 o'clock.

Many digital clocks show 24-hour time. This starts at 00:00 or 0000 as midnight and goes to 12:00 or 1200 at midday. But then instead of starting again, the numbers keep going, with 1 o'clock in the afternoon shown as 13:00, 2 o'clock as 14:00 and so on. The time goes up to 23:59, which is one minute to midnight, and then starts again at 00:00.

Time in the morning is the same on a 12-hour clock and a 24-hour clock. Times in the afternoon on a 24-hour clock have 12 added to the hour that would show on a 12-hour clock:

Hint

Remember that times 'to' the hour are written as minutes past the previous hour – so '10 to 4' is the same as '50 minutes past 3', which we write as 3:50. To find the number for the minutes, subtract the 'minutes to' from 60.

Time	12-hour clock	24-hour clock
10 past 7 in the morning	7:10	07:10
Half past 4 in the afternoon	4:30	16:30 (4 + 12 = 16)
Quarter to 9 in the evening	8:45	20:45 (8 + 12 = 20)

Look at this example to make sure you know how to convert between 12- and 24-hour times.

Example 4

You want to watch a television programme that starts at quarter to 6. A friend will visit you at half past 6, and you want to remember to turn the television off and get ready at 25 past 6.

You set an alarm on your cooker clock to turn the TV on. Your cooker clock uses 24-hour time. What do you need to set it to?

What will the clock on the wall show when you need to turn the TV off?

Method:

Quarter to six is (60 − 15 = 45) minutes past 5. In 12-hour time this is 5:45.

You need to change it to 24-hour time, so add 12 to the hour number:

5 + 12 = 17

You need to set the alarm for 17:45.

As you check the clock on the wall, you need to look out for 25 past 6, which is 6:25. The clock will look like this:

Now try these.

Activity 3

1   You have to catch a bus to the railway station and then take a train. The timetables use the 24-hour clock. The bus goes at 16:55, and the train leaves at 17:20. Show how the time will look on your watch when you get on the bus and when your train leaves.

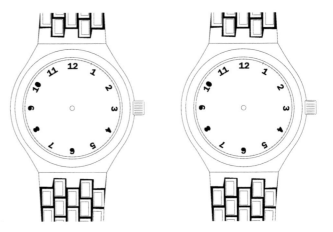

2   There has been a power cut and you have to reset the 24-hour clock on your radio alarm. You listen to the radio to hear a time check. The time is '17 minutes to 4'. It is the afternoon. What do you set your clock to?

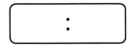

You notice your watch is wrong, so re-set this too. What will your watch look like?

3   A friend asks you to record a TV programme on video for them. It starts at 20 to 7 and ends at 5 past 8 in the evening. Show the times you have to set on the video recorder.

Check your answers with our suggestions before you carry on.

Suggestions for Activity 3

1   16:55 is 5 minutes to 5. On your watch, it will look like this:

17:20 is 20 minutes past 5. On your watch, it will look like this:

2   You need to work out how many minutes past 3 it will be at 17 minutes to 4:

60 − 17 = 43

You need to know what 3 o'clock in the afternoon is in 24-hour time:

3 + 12 = 15

So the time you need to set is

15:43

On your watch, it will look like this:

3   You need to work out how many minutes past 6 it is at 20 to 7:

60 – 20 = 40

Six o'clock in the evening in 24-hour time is

6 + 12 = 18

So you need to set the start time to 18:40

To work out how 8 o'clock in the evening is shown in 24-hour time

8 + 12 = 20

So you need to set the end time to 20:05.

Summary

In this topic you have learned how to use 12- and 24-hour time.

Topic 2 covers these parts of the Common Measures curriculum:

● 'understand the time using 12-hour clocks and 24-hour clocks'

● 'know that midnight is 00:00, or 0000, and 12:00 or 1200 is midday'.

Topic 3: Time and date

Curr. ref: MSS1/L1.1

In this topic, you will find out how we show times and dates. You will need to know how times and dates are shown so that you can find out when things happen and make arrangements for the future.

When would you need to read and understand written times and dates?

You need to understand times and dates in different ways to read timetables, TV and film listings, to check appointment times or times of classes or meetings.

There are lots of other occasions when these skills are useful. You might have thought of different examples.

Writing the time and date

The time of day can be written in different ways. Usually, the time in hours is followed by the time in minutes, with a symbol such as . or : between the numbers. Both 12-hour times and 24-hour times are shown like this.

So 8:40 is the same as 08:40, 8.40 and 08.40.

If seconds are shown, they come after the minutes.

Man runs marathon in 2:57:34

Local man Joseph Franklin completed the Venice marathon in two hours, 57 minutes and 34 seconds yesterday

The date is usually shown in the order: day, month, year. The month might be shown as a word, or shortened word – January, or Jan. It might be shown as a number. Months are counted from January, with January as 01 and December as 12. The year might be shown with two digits, or four: 05 or 2005.

Month	Abbreviation	Number
January	Jan	1 or 01
February	Feb	2 or 02
March	Mar	3 or 03
April	Apr	4 or 04
May	May	5 or 05
June	Jun	6 or 06
July	Jul	7 or 07
August	Aug	8 or 08
September	Sep or Sept	9 or 09
October	Oct	10
November	Nov	11
December	Dec	12

We can write the date 25 December 2005 in all these ways:

25 Dec 2005

25 Dec 05

25-12-05

25.12.2005

Look at this example to make sure you understand times and dates shown in different ways.

Example 5

You have to read out the details of on this security pass to a supervisor on the phone. Fill in the blanks to show what you would say.

Security Pass
Systems Plc

Jilna Shah

Date of Birth:
28.05.1975

Entry hours:
0745-1830

'Jilna Shah was born on …th of … in … The pass lets her into the building between … in the morning and … in the evening.'

Method:

You need to work out which numbers are the day, month and year of her birthday. The first two numbers show the day: 28th. The next two numbers show the month: the fifth month is May. The last four numbers show the year: 1975.

The entry hours are shown in 24-hour time. 0745 is the same as 7.45. You might say 'seven forty-five' or you might say 'quarter to eight'. 1830 is half past six (18 –12 = 6). You might say 'six-thirty' or 'half past six'.

You would say:

'She was born on 28th of May in 1975. The pass lets her into the building between quarter to eight in the morning and half past six in the evening.'

Now try these.

Activity 4

1   Your supervisor asks you to book a flight to Newcastle 'on Friday July 6 at quarter to six in the evening'. The year is 2006. Fill in the time and date you would need to put on the booking form. Show the month as three letters.

Departure time: ☐ ☐ : ☐ ☐

Departure date: ☐ ☐ : ☐ ☐ ☐ : ☐ ☐

2   You have a new answer-phone and have to set the time and date. The format is:

hh:mm:ss (two numbers for the hour, then two numbers for the minutes, then two for the seconds)

DD:MM:YY (two numbers for the day, then two for the month, then two for the year)

It is 12 minutes and 25 seconds past 6 in the evening on 3 February 2006. What do you need to set on the answer-phone?

3   You have offered to meet a visitor at the airport. She has emailed you her flight details. What day and time do you need to be at the airport?

Hi, just to let you know I will be on

Flight: EJ246

Arrival time: 23.35, 11-12-06.

See you there.

Alice

Check your answers with our suggestions before you carry on.

Suggestions for Activity 4

1   Remember that 'quarter to six' is 45 minutes past five.

Departure time:	17:45
Departure date:	06:JUL:06

2   You need to put the time into order: hours-minutes-seconds. Remember to use 24-hour time:

18:12:25

February is the second month, so the date is

03:02:06

3   The time is shown using the 24-hour clock. 23 is 11pm, so 23:35 is 35 minutes past 11, or 25 to 12. The date is shown as day-month-year, so this is 11 December 2006.

Using timetables

One place you often have to read times and dates is in **timetables**.

Sometimes there is no symbol between the hour and minute figures. Then the time looks like this:

0840

Train Times from Cambridge to London				
Outward journey				
Thursday 16 December 2004				
Depart	0840	0940	1045	1155
Arrive	0945	1055	1150	13:05
Changes	0	3	0	3
Duration	1:05	1:15	1:05	1:15

If you use an online timetable you have to give either the time you are going to leave on your journey or the time you want to arrive. The web page will find suitable journeys for you.

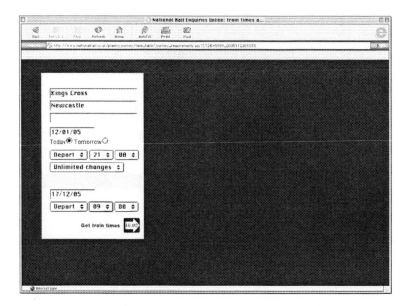

Look at this example to make sure you can use a timetable.

Example 6

Bus Route 255							
Rail station	0900	0920	0940	1000	1030	1055	1125
Highgate Road	0912	0932	0952	1012	1042	1107	1137
Maris Corner	0917	0937	0957	1017	1047	1112	1142
Butts Lane	0928	0948	1008	1028	1058	1123	1153
Cemetery	0931	0951	1011	1031	1101	1126	1156
High Street	0941	1001	1021	1041	1111	1136	1206
Market Square	0949	1009	1029	1049	1119	1144	1214
Grand Hotel	0953	1013	1033	1053	1123	1148	1218
Technical College	1005	1025	1045	1105	1135	1200	1230
Peasbody Estate	1020	1040	1100	1120	1150	1215	1245

Example 6 continued

a)   You want to go to town shopping. You live in Highgate Road. Is there a bus you can get around 11 o'clock? What time will you get to the Market Square?

b)   The next day you want to get a bus from Highgate Road to the Grand Hotel, getting there in time for a meeting at half past 10. What time do you need to get to the Highgate Road bus stop?

Method:

a)   11 o'clock would be shown on the timetable as 1100. Look along the row for Highgate Road for a bus that goes at around 1100. There is one at 1107, which is 7 minutes past 11. It gets to Market Square at 1144, which is 16 minutes to 12 (about quarter to 12).

b)   Look along the row for Grand Hotel until you find a time just before 1030. There is a bus that arrives at 1013. Now look up the column to see when this bus leaves Highgate Road. It leaves at 0932, which is 9:32 or 28 minutes to 10.

Now try Activity 5.

Activity 5

1   Use an online timetable to find out what time you would have to leave Leeds on a Wednesday to get to London by 3 o'clock in the afternoon.

You will need to return to Leeds later, leaving London just after half past 6. What time does the train go, and when will you get to Leeds?

If you can't use an online timetable, use this timetable instead:

Outward journey
Wednesday 20 October 2004

	text me	text me	text me	text me
Depart	11:05	11:40	12:05	12:40
Arrive	13:29	14:00	14:28	15:00
Changes	0	0	0	0
Duration	2:24	2:20	2:23	2:20

EARLIER TRAIN   VIEW DETAILS   LATER TRAIN

Return journey
Wednesday 20 October 2004

Depart	18:50	19:30	19:33	20:00
Arrive	21:05	21:51	22:28	22:45
Changes	0	0	1	1
Duration	2:15	2:21	2:55	2:45
	text me	text me	text me	text me

EARLIER TRAIN   VIEW DETAILS   LATER TRAIN

2   Look at the bus timetable in Example 5 again. If you wanted to catch a bus from Butts Lane at about quarter to ten, which bus would you choose?

What time would it get to the Technical College?

Check your answers with our suggestions before you continue.

Suggestions for Activity 5

1   You will need to leave Leeds on the 12:40 train (20 to 1 in the afternoon) to get to London at 3 o'clock in the afternoon. (In real life, you would need to allow yourself time to get from the station to the meeting place. Then you would need to get the earlier train, leaving at 12:05.)

You could get a train home leaving London at 18:50 (10 to 7 in the evening). It would get to Leeds at 5 past 9.

2   The bus at 0948 is the closest to quarter to 10. It leaves Butts Lane at 9:48, which is 12 minutes to 10. It gets to the Technical College at 10:25, or 25 past 10.

Summary

In this topic you have learned how to recognise and use different ways of showing the time and date.

Topic 3 helps you cover these parts of the Common Measures curriculum:

● 'understand and use common date formats'

● 'understand and use common time formats'.

Topic 4: Time intervals

Curr. ref: MSS1/L1.1

In this topic, you will find out how to add and subtract periods of time and work out **time intervals**.

When might you need to add together two or more periods of time?

When would you need to work out how many hours and minutes will pass between two times?

You will need to add together periods of time if you want to work out how long it will take to complete two or more tasks or journeys that take a known time to complete.

You will need to work out how much time passes between a start and finish time if you want to find out how long an event will last or how long a journey will take.

There are lots of occasions when these skills are useful. You might have thought of different examples.

Adding times together

Sometimes you might have several things to do, or parts of a journey to make, and you need to add together the times each will take to find out the total amount of time to allow.

If you know how long an event takes and when it starts, you can work out when it will finish. You need to add the amount of time it will take to the starting time.

Look at this example to make sure you know how to add times together.

Example 7

You are paid an hourly rate for your work. During the week, you worked the following times:

Monday morning	3:00 hours
Monday afternoon	4:00 hours
Wednesday morning	3:00 hours
Wednesday afternoon	1:30 hours
Friday morning	2:45 hours
Friday afternoon	3:45 hours

a) How many hours did you work each day? How many hours will you be paid for?

b) Each day, you started your work in the afternoon at 14:00. What time did you finish work each day?

Method:

(a) First, you need to add up the two times for each day. Remember that there are 60 minutes in an hour:

Monday: 3:00 + 4:00 = 7:00 hours

Wednesday: 3:00 + 1:30 = 4:30 hours

Friday: 2:45 + 3:45 = (2 + 3) hours and (45 + 45) minutes

= 5 hours 90 minutes

= 6 hours 30 minutes

Then add up the times from all three days:

7:00 + 4:30 + 6:30 = (7 + 4 + 6) hours and (30 + 30 minutes)

= 17 hours 60 minutes

= 18 hours.

Example 7 continued

b) You need to add the number of hours and minutes you worked each afternoon to your starting time, 14:00.

Monday   14:00

                            + 4:00

                            18:00

Wednesday   14:00

                            + 1:30

                            15:30

Friday   14:00

                            + 3:45

                            17:45

Now try these.

Activity 6

1   In a competition, you have won 10 hours at the gym to use over five days. You have been for these times. How long have you been for all together?

Monday: 1 hour 15 minutes

Tuesday: 2 hours 30 minutes

Wednesday: 1 hour 45 minutes

Thursday: 2 hours 25 minutes

**Activity 6
continued**

2   You are watching a pay-per-view TV channel in a motel.
You can watch five hours for free, but after that you
must pay for it. Can you watch the first three films in the
list without paying?

Motel

Pay-per-view films

First 5 hours free!

The Day after Tomorrow	2 hours 4 minutes
The Blair Witch Project	1 hour 26 minutes
Men in Black II	1 hour 28 minutes
Troy	2 hours 43 minutes

3   You leave your home at 10:35 and take a 20-minute bus
ride to town. You want to go to the hairdresser, which
will take one hour and 15 minutes. It will take 10
minutes to walk from the hair-dressers to the café where
you are meeting a friend. Will you be able to get there
for 12:30?

Check your answers with our suggestions before you carry on.

Suggestions for Activity 6

1   You need to add together all these times:

1 hour 15 minutes + 2 hours 30 minutes + 1 hour 45 minutes + 2 hours 25 minutes

= (1 + 2 + 1 + 2) hours and (15 + 30 + 45 + 25) minutes

= 6 hours and 115 minutes

= 7 hours and 55 minutes

You could have written it like this:

$$
\begin{array}{r}
1{:}15 \\
+\ 2{:}30 \\
+\ 1{:}45 \\
+\ \underline{2{:}25} \\
7{:}55
\end{array}
$$

2   You need to add up the lengths of the three films and see if the answer is less than five hours:

The Day After Tomorrow	2:04
The Blair Witch Project	1:26
Men in Black II	<u>1:28</u>
	4:58

The films come to less than five hours all together, so you can watch all three without paying.

3   Start from the time you leave home and add on the times each stage will take:

	10:35 +
bus ride:	<u>0:20</u>
	10:55 +
hairdresser:	<u>1:15</u>
	12:10 +
walk:	<u>0:10</u>
	12:20

12:20 is before 12:30, so you do have enough time.

Subtracting times

If you know when an event starts and when it finishes, you can work out how long it will take by taking away the start time from the end time.

If you know how long an event takes you can subtract this from the finish time to see when it starts.

Example 8

a) Your train leaves at 10:15. It takes you 35 minutes to drive to the station, up to 10 minutes to park and 5 minutes to buy a ticket. What is the latest time you can leave home?

b) You decided to leave at quarter past 9, and you got to the station at 10 o'clock. How long did it take you?

Method:

a) First, you need to add up the times of the things you have to do:

35 + 10 + 5 minutes = 50 minutes

Next, subtract 50 minutes from the time you need to be at the station.

Example 8 continued

You need to be at the station at 10:15, so you must leave 50 minutes before this.

$$10:15$$
$$- \underline{00:50}$$
$$09:25$$

b) You need to take away the time you left from the time you got to the station:

$$10:00$$
$$- \underline{09:15}$$
$$0:45$$

It took 45 minutes.

Now try these.

Activity 7

1 Your plane leaves London at 16:15. You have to allow at least 1 hour 30 minutes check-in time. It will take you 50 minutes to get to the airport. When do you have to leave home?

Your flight lands at Glasgow at 17:55. How long is the flight?

2 A plumber has an appointment at a house at 11:35. It takes 25 minutes to get there. At half past nine, he gets a call asking him to deal with a burst pipe. It will take 45 minutes to deal with the burst pipe, and 20 minutes to get to and from the place. Can he still get to his appointment at 11:35 if he fixes the burst pipe? What is the latest time he can leave?

Activity 7 continued

3   A woman works in the bar at a theatre. She has to make up drinks orders for the interval. She has 35 drinks to make up, taking two minutes each. The interval is at half past nine. What is the latest time she can start making up the drinks?

Check your answers with our suggestions before you carry on.

Suggestions for Activity 7

1   First you need to work out how much time it will take you to get to the airport and check in:

1 hour 30 minutes + 50 minutes

= 1 hour + (30 + 50) minutes

= 1 hour 80 minutes

= 2 hours 20 minutes

You might have written it like this:

Check-in	1:30 +
Drive to airport	0:50
	2:20

Either way is fine.

You need to leave 2 hours 20 minutes before 16:15:

$$16:15$$
$$- \ 2:20$$
$$13:55$$

Your flight lasts from 16:15 to 17:55 so it is

$$17:55$$
$$- \ 16:15$$
$$1:40$$

1 hour 40 minutes.

2   You need to add up the stages of his journey and the amount of time it will take to fix the pipe.

25 minutes + 45 minutes + 20 minutes

= 90 minutes

= 1 hour 30 minutes

It is half past nine (9:30) so in 1 hour and 30 minutes it will be 11 o'clock. He does have time to fix the pipe.

Take away 1 hour 30 minutes from 11:35 to see when he has to leave:

11:35

− 1:30
_____

10:05

He has to leave at 5 past 10.

3   First, you need to work out how long it will take her to make the drinks:

$35 \times 2 = 70$ minutes

= 1 hour 10 minutes

She needs to start 1 hour 10 minutes before half past nine:

21:30

− 1:10
_____

20:20

If you used 12-hour time, you would have written it like this:

9:30

− 1:10
_____

8:20

She has to start at 20 past 8.

Summary

In this topic you have learned how to add and subtract periods of time and work out time intervals.

> Topic 4 helps you cover this part of the Common Measures curriculum:
>
> ● 'add and subtract times in hours and minutes'.

Section 3: Measuring

Section 3: Measuring

In this section you will practise working with measurements. You will find out about measuring and calculating length, distance, weight, temperature and volume. You will learn how to use different metric measurements, such as kilometres, metres and centimetres, grams and kilograms, and litres.

Reasons for completing this section

Thinking about the things in this section will enable you to:

● measure and understand the sizes of objects

● understand the distances between places

● find out how heavy things are and understand weights

● measure and compare temperatures

● measure and understand volumes and capacities.

Resources

● You will need a ruler and a tape measure for your work on Topic 1.

● You will need a set of kitchen or postage scales for your work on Topic 3.

● You will need a thermometer for your work on Topic 4.

● You will need a measuring jug for your work on Topic 5.

Topic 1: Measuring length

In this topic, you will find out about measuring the **length**, **breadth** and **height** of objects and spaces.

How tall are you?

When might you need to measure and compare the length or height of two things?

Curr. ref: MSS1/L1.4; L1.6; L1.7

You might have put your height in **metres** and **centimetres** (such as 1 metre 80 centimetres) or in feet and inches (such as 5 feet 8 inches). Metres and centimetres are **metric units**. Most things these days are measured in metres and centimetres. Feet and inches are called **imperial units**.

You need to compare sizes in lots of situations. For example, if you were buying a new washing machine, you would measure the space under your worktop where you want to put it, and make sure you chose a washing machine short enough to fit the space.

Using a ruler or tape

Metric measures of length are millimetres, centimetres and metres. Look at this picture of part of a ruler:

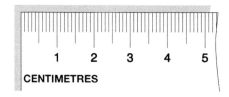

10 millimetres (mm) = 1 centimetre (cm)

100 cm = 1 metre (m).

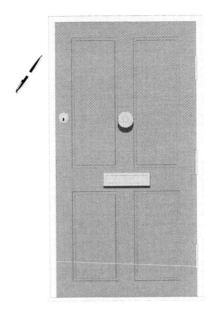

- An uncooked grain of rice is about 2 mm wide by 7 mm long.

- A pen is about 15 cm long.

- A standard door is about 2 m high.

To measure small things, you would probably use a ruler. To measure bigger things, like the length of a room or garden, you would probably use a tape measure.

To measure accurately, line up one end of the object with the first mark on the ruler or tape measure and hold the ruler or tape straight against the object. See which mark the other end comes to.

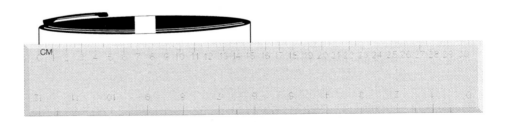

This pen is 15 cm long.

Try **estimating** the size of things before measuring them. This means deciding how big you think something is. Then check your estimate by measuring.

Example 1

How wide is the door in the room you are in?

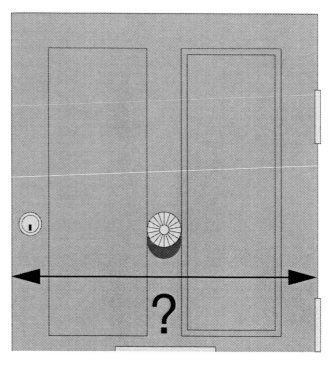

I think the door in my room is 1 metre wide.

I used a tape measure to measure it. It's 83.5 cm. My estimate wasn't very close.

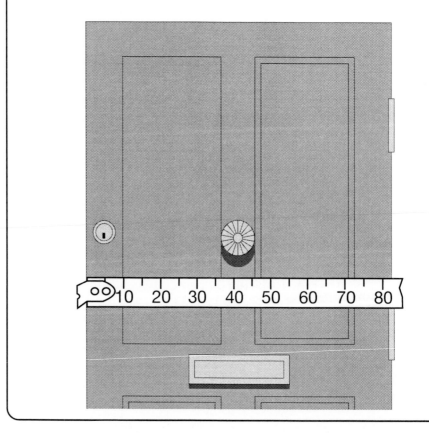

Now try some yourself.

Activity 1

> 1   How long do you think your lower leg is, from knee to ankle? Write down your estimate, and then measure your leg. How good was your estimate?
>
> 2   Look at the room you are in. How long do you think it is? How wide do you think it is? Measure it to see if you are right.

Take a look at our suggestions before you carry on.

Suggestions for Activity 1

1   Here are my answers:

Estimate: 30 cm

Measured length: 35 cm

Comment: a reasonable estimate.

2   Here are my answers:

Estimate: 5 metres

Measured length: 4.70 m (4 m 70 cm)

Comment: that was quite a good estimate.

Between marks

Not all the divisions on a ruler or tape are labelled. On a ruler, each centimetre is marked but the millimetres are not labelled – they are too small! You have to count how many millimetres.

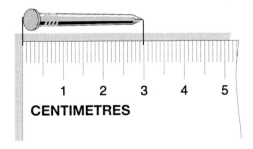

This nail is 3 cm long.

Sometimes, the end of the thing you are measuring comes between two numbered marks.

This tape measure is labelled every 10 centimetres, with marks at 5 centimetres between these.

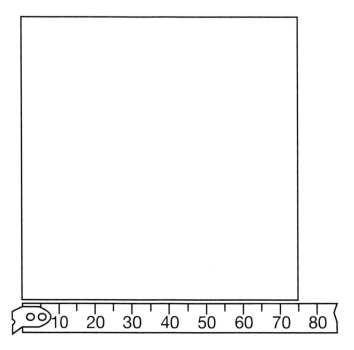

The paving slab is halfway between 70 cm and 80 cm, so it's 75 cm long.

Activity 2

1   You want to build a shelf to hold DVDs. It needs to be big enough! How tall is the DVD case?

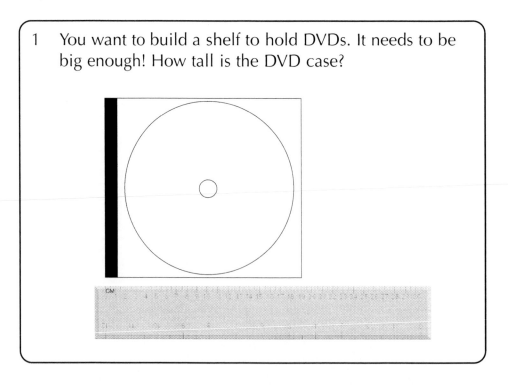

Activity 2 continued

2   You have run out of screws. Before you go to buy some more, you need to measure the last screw you have to make sure you buy the same size. How long is this screw?

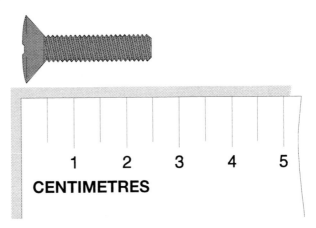

3   How far is it across the head of the screw?

Hint

Draw lines from the edge of the screw head down to the ruler to help you measure it.

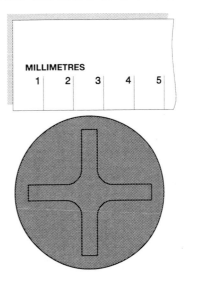

Check your answers against ours before you move on.

Suggestions for Activity 2

1   The DVD case is 19 cm tall.

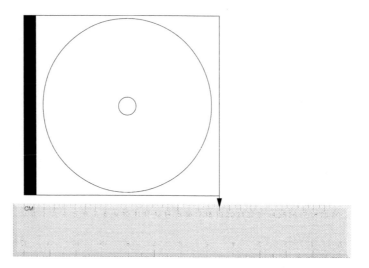

2   The end of the screw is halfway between 2 and 3 cm, so the
     screw is 2.5 cm long.

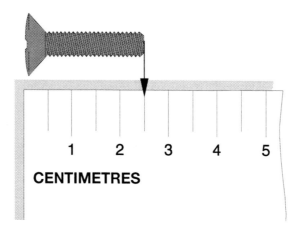

3   The screw head is 5 mm wide.

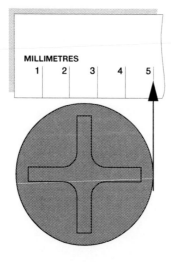

Changing units

10 millimetres
= 1 centimetre
100 centimetres
= 1 metre

Sometimes you will need to change between millimetres and centimetres, or centimetres and metres.

Example 2

You are making Christmas cards for a craft stall. You want to add a bow, which takes 10 cm of ribbon, to each card. You plan to make 50 cards. How many metres of ribbon do you need?

Method:

You need to work out how many centimetres of ribbon you need:

10 x 50 = 500 cm

Then divide by 100 to change this to metres:

500 ÷ 100 = 5 m

Now try these.

Activity 3

1   You are fitting kitchen cabinets. The gap for the last cabinet is 80 cm. The sizes of cabinets are shown in millimetres. Which size should you look for?

2   Thirty children in a class each need 20 cm of string for a project. How many metres of string will they use all together?

3   You want to buy 30 cm of fabric. The fabric is sold by the metre. What should you ask for?

Check your answers with our suggestions before you carry on.

Suggestions for Activity 3

1   You need to work out

$80 \times 10 = 800$ mm

2   You need to work out

$(30 \times 20) \div 100 =$

$600 \div 100 = 6$ m

3   You need to work out

$30 \div 100 = 0.3$ m

Imperial sizes

A few years ago, most people used imperial measures. You may still come across these occasionally. Imperial units for measuring length are inches, feet and yards.

12 inches (in) = 1 foot (ft)

3 feet (ft) = 1 yard (yd)

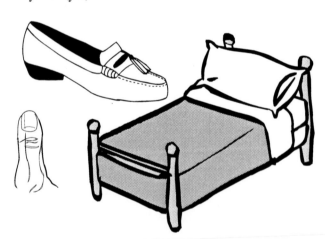

● The top joint of your thumb is about an inch long.

● A shoe to fit an adult is about a foot long.

● A standard size bed is about 2 yards, or 6 feet, long.

Many rulers show centimetres on one edge and inches on the other. Some tape measures show metres on one side and feet on the other.

If you live in an old house, the size of the rooms is probably a bit odd in metres and centimetres, but an exact number of feet and inches.

Example 3

A bathroom is tiled with tiles that are 6 inches square. There are 29 tiles along the wall. How long is the wall?

Method:

There are 12 inches in a foot, so each tile is half a foot wide. The bathroom is

$29 \div 2 = 14\frac{1}{2}$ feet long, or 14 feet 6 inches.

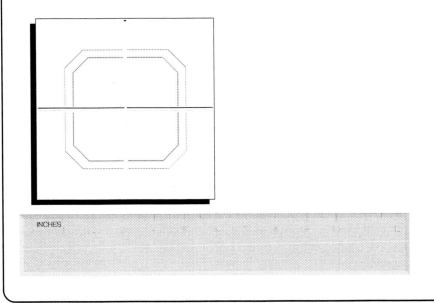

INCHES

Now try some yourself.

Activity 4

1 Your garden is 30 yards long. You can buy 100 feet of hosepipe for £20. Will it reach to the end of your garden?

2 Your window is 5 feet 6 inches wide. You have bought two curtains in a jumble sale that are ready to hang. Each curtain is 36 inches along the top. Will they be big enough for your window?

Check your answers with our suggestions before moving on.

Suggestions for Activity 4

1   You need to work out how long the garden is in feet. There are 3 feet in a yard, so the garden is

$30 \times 3 = 90$ feet long.

The hosepipe is long enough.

2   You need to work out the size of the curtains in feet and inches, or the size of the window in just inches. There are 12 inches in a foot, so the window is

$(5 \times 12) + 6$

$= 60 + 6$

$= 66$ inches wide.

The curtains are

$36 \times 2 = 72$ inches wide.

Or you could convert the curtains to feet:

$36 \div 12 = 3$ feet

$3 \times 2 = 6$ feet.

The curtains are big enough.

Comparing sizes

Although we use metric units now, many old things were made in imperial units so it is useful to know how they compare.

● An inch is about 2.5 cm

● A foot is about 30 cm

● A yard is a bit less than a metre – about 90 cm.

Example 4

A room is 8 feet by 12 feet. You want to buy a rug that is 3 m long. Will it fit in the room?

Method:

The room is 8 feet wide, which is a bit less than 3 yards. The rug is 3 m long, which is a bit more than 3 yards, so it won't fit that way round.

The room is 12 feet long, which is 4 yards. Four yards is more than 3 metres, so the rug will fit. To check:

4 x 90 cm = 3.6 m

Now try these.

Activity 5

1   You have a scarf that is 1 foot wide. You want to stitch a fringe on each end. The fringe is sold in lengths of half a metre. How many lengths do you need to buy?

2   You have an old gardening book that tells you to plant seeds 6 inches apart. How many centimetres apart should they be? Your vegetable plot is 3 m long. About how many seeds do you need for each row?

3   You need to put a new roof on a shed. The shed is 8 feet wide. You can buy roofing felt in widths of 2 m and of 3 m. Which should you buy?

Now check your answers with our suggestions before you move on.

Suggestions for Activity 5

1   One foot is about 30 cm. Each length is 50 cm, so you will have

$$50 - 30 = 20 \text{ cm}$$

left after trimming one end. This isn't enough to trim the other end, so you will need to buy two lengths.

> **Hint**
> If you are measuring spacing for something like seeds, remember that there is one at each end (so one at zero on the tape measure).
> This makes 20 + 1 = 21 seeds.

2   One foot (12 inches) is about 30 cm, so 6 inches is about 15 cm. The seeds need to be 15 cm apart. The row can be 3 m long, which is 300 cm:

$$300 \text{ cm} \div 15 \text{ cm} = 20$$

So you need about 20 seeds for each row.

3   One foot is about 30 cm, so 8 feet is $8 \times 30 = 240$ cm. This is 2.4 m. Roofing felt that is 2 m wide will be too narrow; you should buy roofing felt that is 3 m wide.

Summary

In this topic you have learned how to estimate, measure and compare the sizes of things using metric and imperial measures of length.

> Topic 1 helps you cover these parts of the Common Measures curriculum:
>
> ● 'know how to use metres, centimetres and millimetres'
>
> ● 'read measurements to the nearest mark on a ruler'
>
> ● 'know the relationship between millimetres, centimetres and metres'.

Topic 2: Measuring distance

Curr. ref: MSS1/L1.1; L1.5

In this topic you will practise finding the **distances** between places. You will use charts and maps. Distances between places are measured in **kilometres**, or in **miles**. Road signs and maps in the UK use miles.

How far is it from your home to the nearest shopping centre?

Can you think of a time when it is useful to be able to understand and work out distances between places?

You probably wrote something like '3 miles' or '10 kilometres'. Kilometres are a metric measure of distance.

1000 metres (m) = 1 kilometre (km)

Miles are an imperial measure of distance. A mile is 1,760 yards. A mile is a bit less than 2 kilometres. As most maps and road signs in the UK use miles, we will work with miles.

It's useful to know how far apart places are if you're planning a trip or if your work involves travelling from place to place.

Mileage charts

If you have to plan a trip, it's useful to look at a **mileage chart**. This shows you how far it is between places.

EDINBURGH									
290	Birmingham								
373	102	Cardiff							
496	185	228	Dover						
193	110	208	257	Leeds					
214	90	165	270	73	Liverpool				
412	118	150	81	191	198	London			
222	86	173	285	41	34	201	Manchester		
112	207	301	360	94	155	288	141	Newcastle	
186	129	231	264	25	97	194	66	82	York

To read the chart, find where you want to start from and where you want to go to. Then follow the rows and columns until they meet.

Example 5

How far is it from Cardiff to Manchester?

Method:

You need to see where the column for Cardiff and the row for Manchester meet and read off the distance:

EDINBURGH									
290	Birmingham								
373	102	Cardiff							
496	185	228	Dover						
193	110	208	257	Leeds					
214	90	165	270	73	Liverpool				
412	118	150	81	191	198	London			
222	86	173	285	41	34	201	Manchester		
112	207	301	360	94	155	288	141	Newcastle	
186	129	231	264	25	97	194	66	82	York

Answer: 173 miles

Now try these.

Activity 6

	Roscoff	Cherbourg	Le Havre	Dieppe	Calais	Zeebrugge	Hook of Holland
Amsterdam	536	476	361	309	231	165	53
Barcelona	714	784	802	742	861	872	976
Berlin	866	812	700	667	579	512	410
Bordeaux	323	384	425	423	545	557	677
Brussels	403	351	239	208	126	71	114
Cannes	763	785	688	708	746	758	863
Cologne	541	479	364	328	263	198	178
Florence	949	936	836	834	860	821	876
Frankfurt	616	590	493	436	377	309	304
Geneva	570	555	459	464	517	529	568

1   You want to go on holiday to Florence, crossing the Channel and then driving. Use the mileage chart above. How far is it to Florence from Calais?

2   Which port is closest to Florence?

3   You will come back via Cologne in Germany.

   a)   How far is it from Cologne to the port you chose?

   b)   How far is it from Cologne to Calais?

   c)   Which would be the best port to use?

Now check your answers with our suggestions before you carry on.

Suggestions for Activity 6

1   You need to find the row for Florence and go along it until it meets the column for Calais.

	Roscoff	Cherbourg	Le Havre	Dieppe	Calais	Zeebrugge	Hook of Holland
Amsterdam	536	476	361	309	231	165	53
Barcelona	714	784	802	742	861	872	976
Berlin	866	812	700	667	579	512	410
Bordeaux	323	384	425	423	545	557	677
Brussels	403	351	239	208	126	71	114
Cannes	763	785	688	708	746	758	863
Cologne	541	479	364	328	263	198	178
Florence	949	936	836	834	860	821	876
Frankfurt	616	590	493	436	377	309	304
Geneva	570	555	459	464	517	529	568

The distance in 860 miles.

2   You need to look along the row for Florence and find the shortest distance, then see which port is named at the top of the column. The shortest distance is 821 miles, from Zeebrugge.

3   a)   You need to look along the Cologne row until you get to the Zeebrugge column. The distance in 198 miles.

   b)   Check the distance from Calais to Cologne: 263 miles.

   c)   Zeebrugge is the best port to use as it's closest to both Cologne and Florence.

Adding distances

Many trips have more than one stop. You need to add together the distances to find out how far you will have to travel.

Example 6

A salesman has to travel from Edinburgh to York, then on to London, and then back to Edinburgh. How far will he travel?

Use the mileage chart to find the distances between Edinburgh and York; York and London; London and Edinburgh.

EDINBURGH									
290	Birmingham								
373	102	Cardiff							
496	185	228	Dover						
193	110	208	257	Leeds					
214	90	165	270	73	Liverpool				
412	118	150	81	191	198	London			
222	86	173	285	41	34	201	Manchester		
112	207	301	360	94	155	288	141	Newcastle	
186	129	231	264	25	97	194	66	82	York

Edinburgh to York is 186 miles.

EDINBURGH									
290	Birmingham								
373	102	Cardiff							
496	185	228	Dover						
193	110	208	257	Leeds					
214	90	165	270	73	Liverpool				
412	118	150	81	191	198	London			
222	86	173	285	41	34	201	Manchester		
112	207	301	360	94	155	288	141	Newcastle	
186	129	231	264	25	97	194	66	82	York

London to York is 194 miles.

Example 6 continued

Hint

If you add up the distance from Edinburgh to London via York (186 + 194 = 380 miles), you will see it is less than the distance between London and Edinburgh. The distance in the chart shows how far it is on the best roads (usually motorways), as this is usually the quickest route. But it is not always the shortest route.

EDINBURGH								
290	Birmingham							
373	102	Cardiff						
496	185	228	Dover					
193	110	208	257	Leeds				
214	90	165	270	73	Liverpool			
412	118	150	81	191	198	London		
222	86	173	285	41	34	201	Manchester	
112	207	301	360	94	155	288	141	Newcastle
186	129	231	264	25	97	194	66	82	York

London to Edinburgh is 412 miles.

The total trip is

$$186$$
$$+\ 194$$
$$+\ \underline{412}$$
$$\underline{792}$$

Answer: 792 miles

Now try these.

Activity 7

1　You use a hire car to go from London to Cardiff, from Cardiff to Liverpool and then back to London. You pay 10p for each mile you drive. How many miles must you pay for?

2　You live in Newcastle and you want to buy a second-hand car trailer. There is one for sale in Leeds and one in York. Which one is closest?

Check your answers with our suggestions before you go on.

Suggestions for Activity 7

1   You need to look up all the distances and then add them together:

EDINBURGH								
290	Birmingham							
373	102	Cardiff						
496	185	228	Dover					
193	110	208	257	Leeds				
214	90	165	270	73	Liverpool			
412	118	150	81	191	198	London		
222	86	173	285	41	34	201	Manchester	
112	207	301	360	94	155	288	141	Newcastle
186	129	231	264	25	97	194	66	82	York

London to Cardiff is 150 miles.

EDINBURGH								
290	Birmingham							
373	102	Cardiff						
496	185	228	Dover					
193	110	208	257	Leeds				
214	90	165	270	73	Liverpool			
412	118	150	81	191	198	London		
222	86	173	285	41	34	201	Manchester	
112	207	301	360	94	155	288	141	Newcastle
186	129	231	264	25	97	194	66	82	York

Cardiff to Liverpool is 165 miles.

EDINBURGH								
290	Birmingham							
373	102	Cardiff						
496	185	228	Dover					
193	110	208	257	Leeds				
214	90	165	270	73	Liverpool			
412	118	150	81	191	198	London		
222	86	173	285	41	34	201	Manchester	
112	207	301	360	94	155	288	141	Newcastle
186	129	231	264	25	97	194	66	82	York

Liverpool to London is 198 miles.

The total is:

150

+ 165

+ 198

513 miles

2　You need to compare the distances from Newcastle to Leeds and Newcastle to York.

EDINBURGH								
290	Birmingham							
373	102	Cardiff						
496	185	228	Dover					
193	110	208	257	Leeds				
214	90	165	270	73	Liverpool			
412	118	150	81	191	198	London		
222	86	173	285	41	34	201	Manchester	
112	207	301	360	94	155	288	141	Newcastle
186	129	231	264	25	97	194	66	82	York

Newcastle to Leeds is 94 miles.

EDINBURGH								
290	Birmingham							
373	102	Cardiff						
496	185	228	Dover					
193	110	208	257	Leeds				
214	90	165	270	73	Liverpool			
412	118	150	81	191	198	London		
222	86	173	285	41	34	201	Manchester	
112	207	301	360	94	155	288	141	Newcastle
186	129	231	264	25	97	194	66	82	York

Newcastle to York is 82 miles.

So the trailer in York is closer.

Using maps

You won't always have a mileage chart you can use. If you want to find the distance between local places, or smaller towns that aren't listed in mileage charts, you will need to use a **map**.

A map shows the **scale** it uses. This tells you how the distance on the map relates to the distance in the real area the map shows.

There are two ways of showing scale:

● It might say something like '1 inch : 1 mile' or '4 inches : 1 mile'. This means that every mile in the real world is shown by 1 inch (or 4 inches) on the map.

● It might say something like '1 : 50,000'. This means that one unit on the map stands for 50,000 of the same unit in the real world. So 1 inch is 50,000 inches, or 1 centimetre is 50,000 centimetres (= 500 metres = half a kilometre).

There's often a bar to show the scale so that you can measure it with a ruler. It looks like this:

If you use an on-line map, such as www.multimap.co.uk, you can switch between scales. You can zoom in to see more detail or zoom out to see where the place is in the whole area.

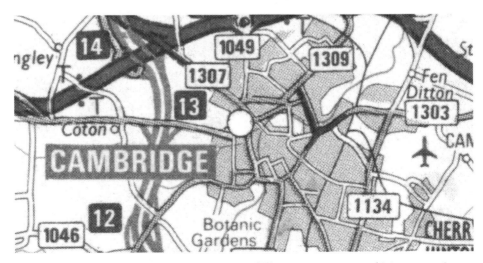

The scale of this map is 1 : 50,000. This means everything on the map is 50,000 times bigger in real life.

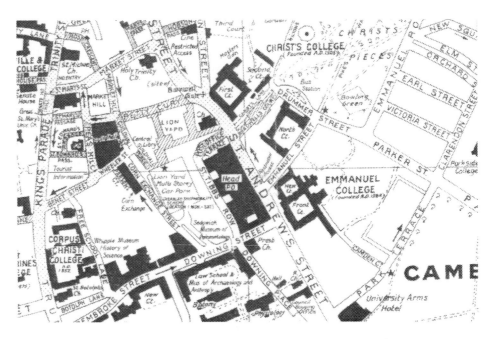

The scale of this map is 1 : 25,000, so everything is 25,000 times bigger in the real world.

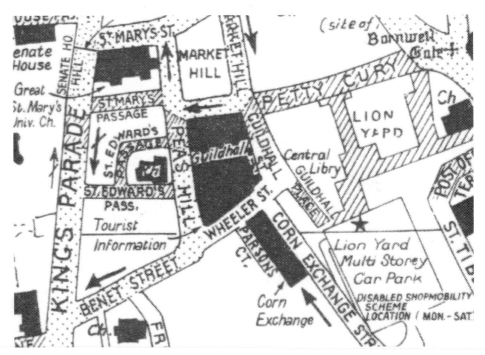

The scale of this map is only 1 : 5,000. You can see much more detail.

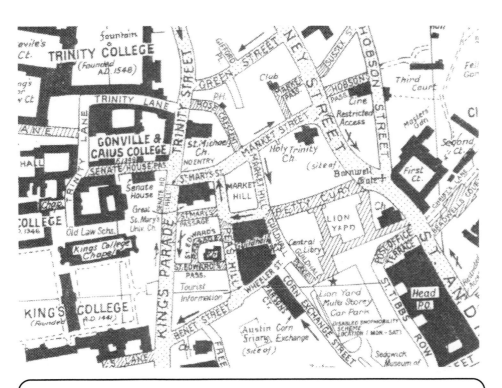

Example 7

Look at the last map above.

You want to walk from Trinity College to the junction of King's Parade with Bene't Street and then along Bene't Street to Lion Yard Shopping Centre. How far is it?

Method:

Use a ruler to measure the distance from Trinity College to the junction. This is a fairly straight line, so your measurement will be reasonably accurate.

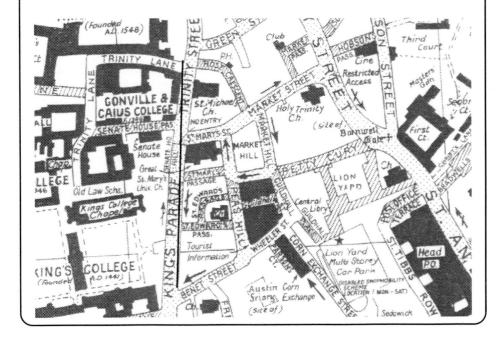

Example 7 continued

The distance is 6 cm.

Now measure along Bene't Street from the junction to the shopping centre. The distance is 3 cm.

The total distance on the map is 9 cm. The scale is 1 : 5,000, so it is

9 x 5,000 = 45,000 cm.

There are 100 cm in a metre, so it is

45,000 ÷ 100 = 450 m, or about half a kilometre.

Now try these.

Activity 8

Tip
Use the map on the previous page.

Hint
Remember to break the distance down into sections that are nearly straight lines.

Hint
As the scale is given in inches, you should measure the map in inches to make the calculation easy.

1   You have gone to Cambridge for the day. There is a bus station at Drummer Street. You want to walk to King's College Chapel. How far is it?

2   Use this map to find out how far it is from Cambridge to St Neots. The scale is 1 inch to 7 miles, so every inch of map shows seven miles of road.

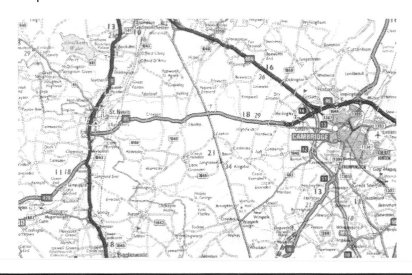

Now check your answers with our suggestions before you carry on.

Suggestions for Activity 8

1   You should have made these measurements:

Along Drummer Street	2 cm
Along Emmanuel Street	3 cm
Emmanuel Street to Petty Cury	4 cm
Along Petty Cury	3 cm
From Petty Cury to King's Parade	3 cm
From King's Parade to King's College Chapel	<u>2 cm</u>
Total distance	<u>17 cm</u>

$17 \times 5{,}000 = 85{,}000$ cm

= 850 metres.

2   You should have measured the distance on the map and found that it's $2\frac{1}{2}$ inches. Each inch is 7 miles, so the distance is

$2.5 \times 7 = 17.5$ miles.

Summary

In this topic you have learned how to find and compare distances using mileage charts and maps.

Topic 2 helps you cover these parts of the Common Measures curriculum:

- 'know that distance is measured in miles or kilometres'

- 'understand and use a mileage chart'

- 'use a simple scale to work out distances on a road map'.

Curr. ref: MSS1/L1.4; L1.6; L1.7

Topic 3: Weight

In this topic you will practise estimating, measuring and comparing weights.

How much do you weigh?

You might have given your weight in **kilograms** (kg) or in **pounds** (lb), or pounds and **stone** (st). Kilograms are **metric weights**. Pounds and stones are **imperial weights**.

Using metric weights

Metric weights are **grams** and **kilograms**.

1,000 grams (g) = 1 kilogram (kg)

You should measure weight in metric units, but you might see the old imperial units used sometimes.

Many foods are sold by weight. For example, you might buy:

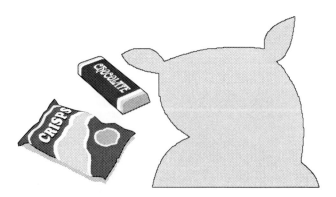

- 500 g of rice; this is about a pound of rice

- 250 g of coffee (about half a pound)

- 100 g of chocolate (a bit less than a quarter of a pound)

- 30 g of crisps (about an ounce)

- 10 g of a spice (about a third of an ounce).

Hint

If you bought ten 500 g packets of rice, you would say you had bought 5 kg rather than 5,000 g.

Heavier things are weighed in kilograms. You might buy:

- 50 kg of sharp sand (about 110 pounds)

- 10 kg chicken food (about 20 pounds)

- 1 kg of nails (about 2 pounds).

Scales show you how many grams or kilograms something weighs. Some scales are digital: they show the weight as a display of numbers.

Other scales have a dial or line of numbers and you have to read the weight from this.

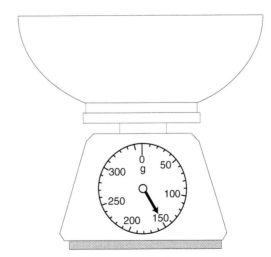

The needle on these scales points to 150 g.

You need to know the **divisions** marked on the scales. You might have to count the marks between numbers.

Example 8   What is the weight of the flour in these scales?

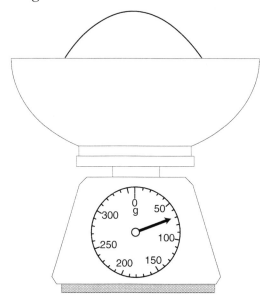

There are four marks between 50 g and 100 g, so each represents 10 g: 60 g, 70 g, 80 g and 90 g. The needle is at the second mark, so the weight is 70 g.

Now try these.

Activity 9   1   How many grams of sugar are there?

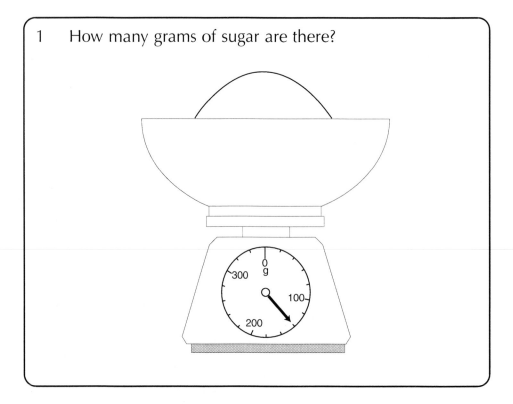

Activity 9 continued

2 What is the person's weight in kilograms?

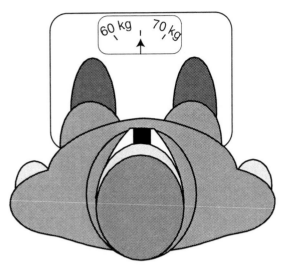

3 How much does the letter weigh?

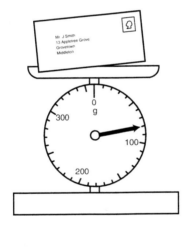

Now check your answers with our suggestions before you move on.

Suggestions for Activity 9

1 There are four marks between 100 g and 200 g, so each marks 20 g: 20 g, 40 g, 60 g, 80 g. The needle is at the second, so there are 100 + 40 = 140 g of sugar.

2   The needle is halfway between 60 kg and 70 kg, so the person weighs 65 kg.

3   There are nine marks between 0 g and 100 g, so there's a mark at every 10 g. The needle is two marks before 100 g, so the letter weighs (100 − 20) = 80 g.

Weighing things

It's useful to have an idea of how much things weigh. It will help you work out the weight of fruit or vegetables to buy in a market, for example, or whether your suitcase will be within the weight limit for a flight.

Try estimating the weight of something before you weigh it. It will help you to get used to measures of weight.

Example 9

a)   Which metric unit would you use to weigh an apple?

b)   How much does an apple weigh?

c)   How much would 20 of these apples weigh? Would you use the same units?

Method:

a)   An apple is quite small, so we would weigh it in grams.

b)   I think an apple weighs 100 g.

This is how much the apple weighs on the scales:

130 g

Example 9 continued

c)   Twenty apples would weigh

130 x 20 = 2,600 g

You would use kilograms if you were weighing a lot of apples:

2,600 g = 2.6 kg.

Now try these. You will need to collect together the things you are going to weigh.

Activity 10

Hint
The weight shown on the label is the weight of sauce – it doesn't include the weight of the jar itself.

a)   How much do 10 tea bags weigh? Estimate and then weigh them.

b)   How heavy is a bottle of sauce? How much would a case of 10 bottles weigh?

c)   How heavy is a book?

Now check your answers with our suggestions before you carry on.

Suggestions for Activity 10

These are our suggestions. Your estimates and measured weights might be different, but they should be roughly similar.

Item	Estimate	Actual weight
10 teabags	25 g	30 g
Bottle of sauce	500 g	450 g
Book	900 g	720 g

A case of ten bottles of sauce would weigh

$450 \times 10 = 4,500$ g

= 4.5 kg.

If your book weighed more than ours, you might have given its weight in kilograms. If you chose a small book, it may have weighed a lot less.

Comparing weights

Most weights are given in metric units now – grams and kilograms. A few years ago, most people used imperial measures of weight – ounces, pounds and stones.

16 ounces (oz) = 1 pound (lb)

14 pounds = 1 stone (st)

You might still come across these weights sometimes.

An ounce is a bit less than 30 g. A pound is a bit less than half a kilogram.

Example 10

Tip
1 st = 14 lb

You have an old ladder with a label that says it can hold up to 20 stone. You weigh 80 kg. Can you safely use the ladder?

Method:

You need to work out roughly what 20 stone is in kilograms.

20 x 14 = 280 lbs

One pound is nearly half a kilogram:

280 ÷ 2 = 140

The ladder will take about 140 kg, so you're safe.

Now try these.

Activity 11

1   You are allowed a bag of 5 kg as hand luggage on a plane. You have weighed your bag on some old bathroom scales and found it is 7 lbs. Can you take it?

2   You are using a recipe your grandmother wrote down. It calls for 4 oz sugar. You only have 150 g left. Do you have enough to make the recipe?

Check your answers with our suggestions before continuing.

Suggestions for Activity 11

1   You need to work out

    $5 \times 2 = 10$ lbs or $7 \div 2 = 3.5$ kg

    You can take your bag.

2   You need to work out

    $4 \times 30 = 120$ g or $150 \div 30 = 5$ oz

    You do have enough sugar.

Summary

In this topic you have learned how to estimate and measure weight.

> Topic 3 helps you cover these parts of the Common Measures curriculum:
>
> ● 'use metric units of weight'
>
> ● 'read scales'
>
> ● 'know the relationship between grams and kilograms'.

Curr. ref: MSS1/L1.4; L1.6; L1.7

Topic 4: Measuring temperature

In this topic you will practise working with temperatures. The **temperature** tells us how hot or cold something is. You will see or hear temperatures mentioned in a weather forecast. You will also come across temperatures in recipes and in other instructions. Temperature is sometimes given in degrees **Celsius** and sometimes in degrees **Fahrenheit**.

At what temperature does water

a)　freeze?

b)　boil?

The temperature in Britain during the day time is usually between 0° Celsius (0°C) on a cold winter's day and 25° Celsius on a hot day in summer. What temperature do you think it is today?

<table>
<tr><td>**Hint**
You might sometimes see Celsius called 'centigrade'.</td></tr>
</table>

Water freezes at 0° Celsius and boils at 100° Celsius.

If you have a thermometer, check the temperature outside. If you don't have a thermometer, check the weather on-line. Use www.bbc.co.uk/weather to find the temperature near you.

Reading temperatures

Many things have to be stored or used in a particular temperature range to be safe. Temperature is measured with a **thermometer**.

Thermometers for different uses show different ranges of temperatures.

This thermometer is used for measuring a person's temperature. It shows the range 35°C to 40°C (95°–104°F).

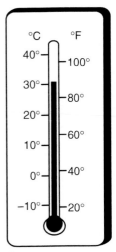

This thermometer shows the temperature outside. It shows the range −10°C to 40°C.

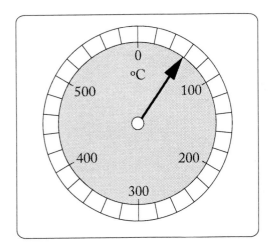

This thermometer is on the wall of an industrial oven. It shows temperatures from 0°C to 500°C.

Example 11

What is the temperature on each thermometer?

a)

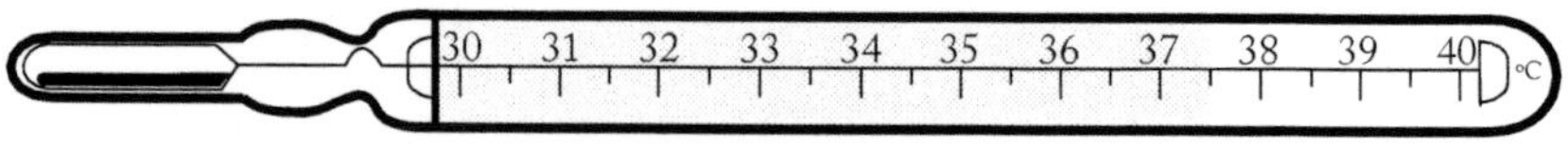

b)

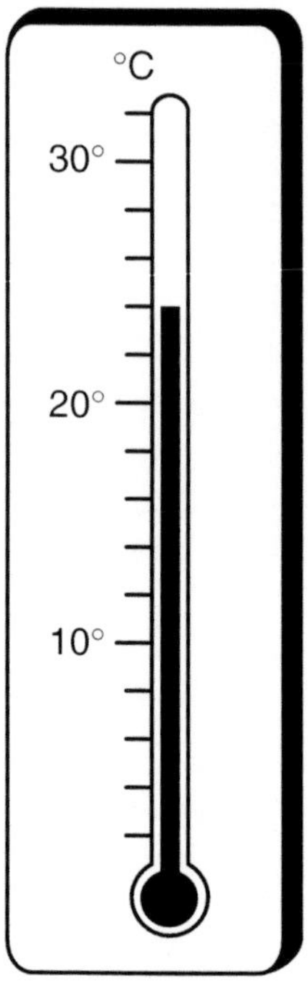

Method:

a)   The temperature is at the mark halfway between 37 and 38, so it's 37.5°C.

b)   There are four divisions between 20 and 30, so the divisions mark every two degrees (22, 24, 26, 28). The reading is at the second mark after 20, so the temperature is 24°C.

Now try these.

Activity 12

What temperature is shown by each of these?

a)

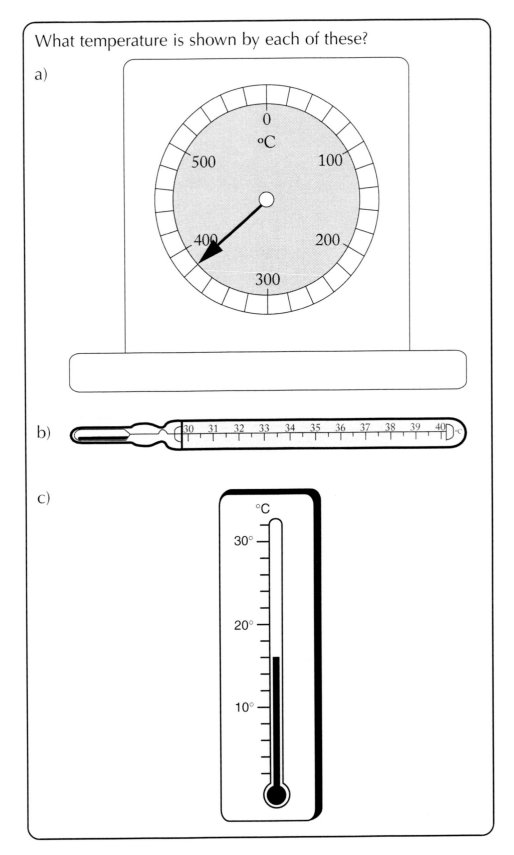

b)

c)

Check your answers with our suggestions before you go on.

Suggestions for Activity 12

a) The temperature is marked every 20 degrees, and the needle is at the mark below 400, so the temperature is 380°C.

b) The reading is on the mark between 38 and 39, so the temperature is 38.5°C.

c) The markings are every two degrees, so the temperature is 16°C.

Understanding temperature

Using the right temperature is often a matter of safety. For example, you should store frozen food below −18°C. That means it must be 18°C colder than the point at which water freezes.

Temperatures used to be shown in degrees Fahrenheit. You will still see these measures sometimes.

Ingredients

1 oz butter (25 g)
1 smallish onion, finely chopped
$\frac{1}{2}$ oz flour (10 g)
3 oz Cheddar cheese (75 g), grated
1 egg yolk
1 tablespoon grated Parmesan cheese

Cook at 180ºC (350ºF)

August temperatures:

35 – 38ºC (95 – 100ºF)

Here are some temperatures in Celsius and Fahrenheit:

Celsius	Fahrenheit
0	32
10	50
20	68
30	86
40	104
50	122

Example 12

Note

Fahrenheit is still used in the USA.

You have instructions with chemicals sent from the USA that they must be stored between 50 and 70°F. The thermometer on the storage tank shows the temperature in degrees Celsius.

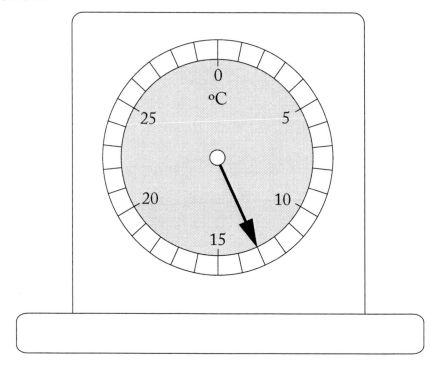

Are the chemicals stored safely?

Method:

Find the range in Fahrenheit on the chart and see whether 13°C falls in this range:

    10   50

    20   68

13°C falls between 10 and 20, so it is in the range 50 – 68°F. The chemicals are stored safely.

Now try these.

Activity 13

1   A recipe for meringue says you must cook it at 150°C. Your cooker shows temperatures in Fahrenheit. What should you set it to?

Celsius	Fahrenheit
100	212
150	302
200	392
250	482
300	572
350	662

2   The thermometer on an old freezer shows the temperature in degrees Fahrenheit. A pack of food has a warning that it must be stored between –12°C and –25°C. Is the food stored safely?

Celsius	Fahrenheit
– 30	– 22
– 20	– 4
– 15	5
– 10	14
– 5	23
0	32
10	50

Activity 13 continued

3   This machine must be turned off if the temperature rises above 600°F. Is it safe to leave it turned on?

Celsius	Fahrenheit
0	32
50	122
100	212
150	302
200	392
250	482
300	572
350	662
400	752

Check your answers with our suggestions before you go on.

Suggestions for Activity 13

1   You need to look up 150°C on the chart – it is 302°F. The oven isn't marked this accurately, so you should set it to 300°F.

2   You need to find where 1°F would be on the chart. Five degrees Fahrenheit is –15°C; –4°F is –20°C. The temperature is between –15°C and –20°C, so the food is stored safely.

3   You need to find 600°F on the chart. The closest is 350°C, which is over 600°F. The temperature on the dial is even higher than this, 370°C. The machine is not safe and must be switched off.

Summary

In this topic you have learned how to measure and understand temperature.

Topic 4 helps you cover these parts of the Common Measures curriculum:

●   'know the standard units for measuring temperature'

●   'read a thermometer'

●   'recognise temperatures in degrees Celsius and degrees Fahrenheit'.

Curr. ref: MSS1/L1.4; L1.6; L1.7

Topic 5: Capacity

In this topic you will learn how to estimate, measure and compare **capacity**, or **volume**. This is the amount of space that something takes up. You will see the volume of liquids shown on cartons and bottles, for instance.

When you buy milk, how much is in each bottle or carton?

What about when you buy juice?

Most people buy milk in cartons of 1, 2, 4 or 6 pints. Juice is usually sold in cartons of 1 litre. Pints are an imperial measure of volume. Litres are a metric measure of volume.

Measuring volume in litres

We usually measure volume using metric units. The metric unit of volume is the **litre**.

1,000 millilitres = **1** litre

To measure a very small amount, you might use a teaspoon. This is the same as 5 millilitres (ml).

To measure larger amounts, you probably use a measuring jug of some kind.

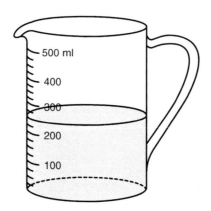

Example 13

If you had to measure out 350 ml of juice for a recipe, where would the liquid come to in this jug?

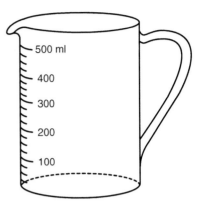

Method:

There are three marks on the jug between 300 ml and 400 ml. These mark 325, 350 and 375 ml. So you need to fill the jug to the middle mark:

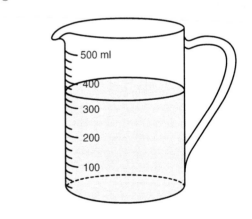

Now try these.

Activity 14

1   How much coffee or tea does your normal cup hold? Estimate the volume first, and write down your estimate. Next, fill your cup with water and then pour the water into a measuring jug.

2   A scientist has to measure 2.8 ml of liquid in this pipette. Where should the liquid come to?

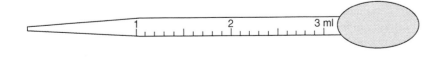

3   How many litres of water has the plumber drained from the system?

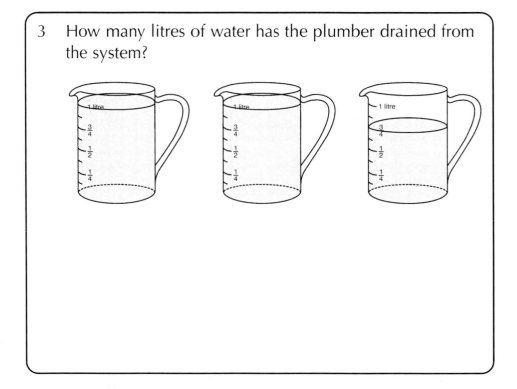

Look at our suggestions when you have given your answers.

Suggestions for Activity 14

1   I think my cup holds 400 ml.

    It actually holds 350 ml.

2   The divisions are marked every 0.1 ml. The pipette should look like this:

3   The plumber has drained two full jugs of one litre and three quarters of another jug, so 2.75 litres.

Changing units

Remember

There are 1,000 millilitres in a litre.

You will sometimes need to change between millilitres and litres.

Example 14

You are cooking for a large party. The recipe you are using calls for 600 ml of milk to make enough for four people. How many litres of milk will you need to make ten times as much?

Method:

You need to work out

$600 \times 10 = 6,000$ ml

$6,000 \div 1,000 = 6$ litres.

Now try these.

Activity 15

1 A nurse has to order enough soup for 100 patients on a ward. Each patient will eat 400 ml of soup. How many litres of soup must the nurse order?

2 Twenty people working in a craft workshop have to share the last 2-litre bottle of glue. How many millilitres of glue can each person use?

Check your answers with our suggestions before you carry on.

Suggestions for Activity 15

1 You need to work out

$(100 \times 400) \div 1,000 =$

$(40,000) \div 1,000 = 40$ litres.

2 First work out how many millilitres are in 2 litres of glue:

$2 \times 1,000 = 2,000$ ml

Then work out

$2,000 \div 20 = 100$ ml each.

Using pints and gallons

You might still see the old, imperial units for measuring volume.

20 fluid ounces (fl oz) = 1 pint (pt)

8 pts = 1 gallon (gal).

A pint is a bit more than half a litre.

A fluid ounce is about 25 ml.

Some measuring jugs show both units.

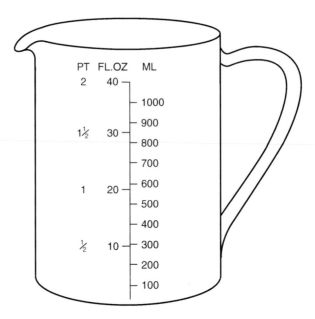

© National Extension College Trust Ltd

Example 15

You have an old gallon can in your shed. You take it to the garage to buy petrol for your lawn mower. About how many litres of petrol can you buy?

Method:

A pint is a bit more than half a litre, so you can get just over a litre for every 2 pints.

There are 8 pints in a gallon, so you can get nearly $4\frac{1}{2}$ litres of petrol.

Now try these.

Activity 16

1   You are mixing up weed-killer. The packet says to use a pint of weed-killer in a gallon of water. You have only a metric measuring jug. How much water should you use with one litre of weed-killer?

2   An old recipe tells you to make up $1\frac{1}{2}$ pints of custard. You prefer to buy custard in the supermarket. It is sold in cartons of 500 ml. How many do you need to buy to be sure you have enough for the recipe?

Check your answers with our suggestions before you carry on.

Suggestions for Activity 16

1   There are 8 pints in 1 gallon, so you have to use eight times as much water as weed-killer. If you use 1 litre of weed-killer, you will need 8 litres of water.

2   A pint is a bit more than half a litre. Two pints would be a bit more than a litre, so a pint and a half is a bit less than a litre. You need to buy 1 litre of custard, which is two cartons of 500 ml.

Summary

In this topic you have learned how to measure volume or capacity.

Topic 5 helps you cover these parts of the Common Measures curriculum:

- 'know the standard units for measuring volume or capacity'

- 'measure volumes'

- 'compare litres and the imperial measures, pints and gallons'.

Section 4: Shapes

Section 4: Shapes

In this section you will practise working with flat shapes. You will find out how to measure or work out how far it is around the edge of a shape. You will work out the area of a rectangle, and draw plans and regular patterns.

Reasons for completing this section

Thinking about the things in this section will enable you to:

- work out how far it is around a shape – this will tell you how much wood you need to frame a picture, for instance

- work out the area of a shape – this will tell you how much carpet you need for a room, for example

- see how shapes fit together – this will help you to place tiles to cover a floor, for instance

- draw plans.

Resources

You will need a ruler, a pair of scissors and either coloured card or white card and crayons for your work on Topic 3. If you don't have any scissors and coloured card or crayons, you can use just white card and a pencil.

You will need a tape measure for your work on Topic 4. A pair of scissors will be useful.

Topic 1: Around the edge

Curr. ref: MSS1/L1.8

In this topic, you will learn how to work out how far it is around a shape.

When might you need to work out how far it is around a flat shape?

You will need to know how far it is around the edge of a shape when you want to put a border around something, such as a wallpaper border around a room, or a brick wall around a patio.

You might have thought of different examples.

Measuring the perimeter

The distance around the edge of a shape is called the **perimeter**. You can measure around a shape in different ways. If the shape has corners, you can work out its perimeter by adding together the length of all its sides.

The sides are measured in units of length or distance, such as centimetres, metres or kilometres.

It's easy to measure the perimeter of a simple shape like a square using a ruler, metre rule or tape measure.

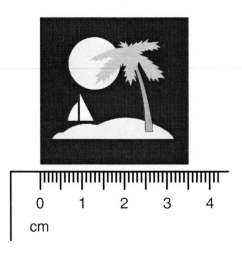

For a very big area, like a playing field or car park, you could use a trundle wheel. This is a wheel you push along the ground. Each time it makes a full turn, it adds one to its count of turns. The number of turns tells you how far you've walked. If a trundle wheel measured a metre with each full turn, it would count 100 turns if you walked 100 metres around a car park.

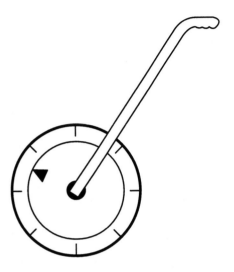

For a rough measurement, you might just pace out the distance, counting each pace as about a metre or yard.

You can pace around or use a trundle wheel to measure the perimeter of any shape – even one that's not regular, like a lake.

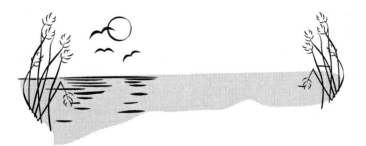

To measure around the perimeter of a small shape that's not regular, you can use a piece of string.

To work out how much edging to buy to go around this cushion, you could lay a piece of string all around the edge, then measure the string.

Example 1

You have some decorative boxes that you want to trim with ribbon. These are the boxes seen from above. How much ribbon will it take to go around each? (Use a ruler.)

Example 1 continued

Hint
Opposite sides of a rectangle are the same length.

Method:

You need to measure all the sides and add them together.

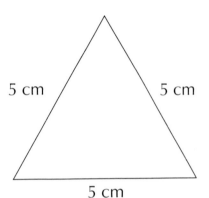

6 cm

4 cm

5 cm   5 cm

5 cm

The sides of the rectangular box are

6 + 6 + 4 + 4 = 20 cm

You will need 20 cm of ribbon.

The sides of the triangular box are

5 + 5 + 5 = 15 cm

You will need 15 cm of ribbon.

Activity 1

1   Measure the perimeter of the top of the desk or table you are working at.

How did you measure it?

2   You are going to be in a carnival parade and need to wear a crown. Measure how far it is around your head so that your crown can be made to fit.

How did you measure it?

3   Go outside and measure the perimeter of the nearest large area – it might be a car park, a garden, or a park, for instance. Draw the rough shape of the area.

How did you measure it?

Check your answers with our suggestions before you go on.

Suggestions for Activity 1

1   The perimeter of my desk is

140 cm + 140 cm + 75 cm + 75 cm = 430 cm

140 cm

75 cm   75 cm

140 cm

I measured it with a tape measure.

2   It is 55 cm around my head. I measured it with a scarf. You might have measured it with a piece of string or paper curved around your head.

3   I measured my front garden.

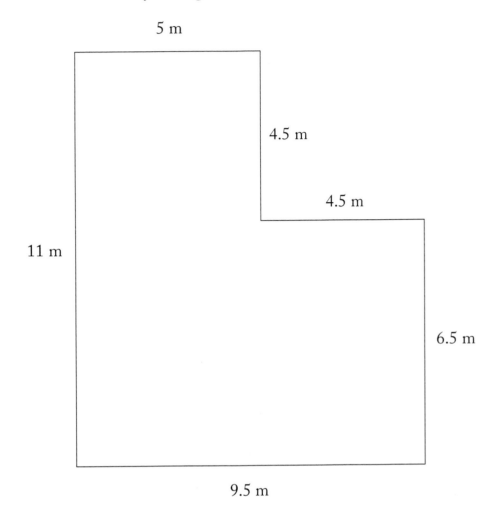

5 m

4.5 m

4.5 m

11 m

6.5 m

9.5 m

The perimeter is

11 m + 5 m + 4.5 m + 4.5 m + 6.5 m + 9.5 m

= 41 m

I measured it by pacing it out.

Using a formula

You might have noticed when you measured the perimeter of your desk or table that there are two long sides that are the same length and two short sides that are the same length.

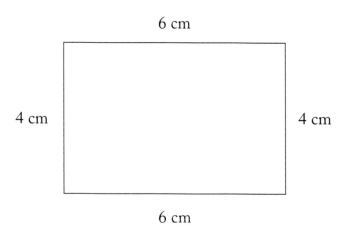

All rectangles share this feature.

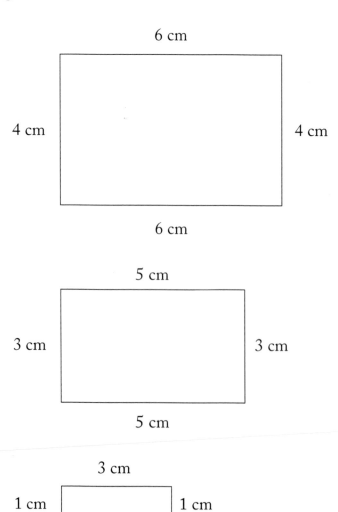

Instead of measuring and adding up four sides, we can measure just one long side and one short side. We can then work out the **perimeter** by using each number twice:

(2 × long side) + (2 × short side) = perimeter

The long side is the length. The short side is the width.

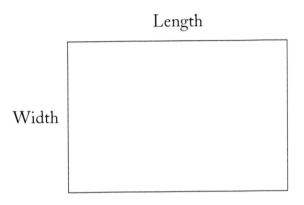

A square is a special type of rectangle and has all four sides the same.

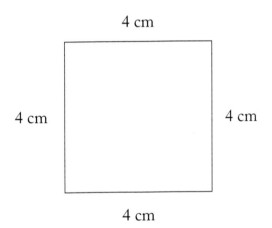

So for the square:

4 × side = perimeter

Example 2

How many metres of lawn edging do you need to go around this lawn?

15 m

8 m

Method:

You need to work out twice the width, plus twice the length:

(2 x 15) + (2 x 8)

= 30 + 16

= 46 m.

Now try these.

Activity 2

1   You need to hang bunting around the tennis court for the local championships. How much bunting do you need?

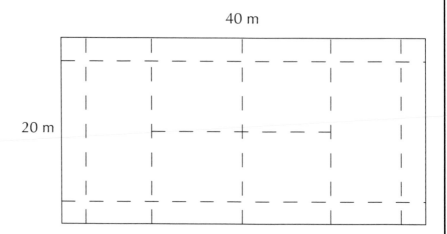

40 m

20 m

Activity 2 continued

2   How much tape does the police officer need to close off this crime scene?

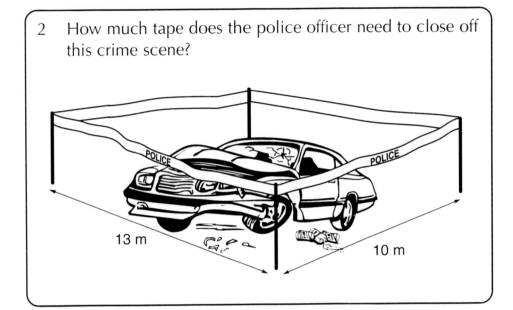

13 m   10 m

Check your answers with our suggestions before you move on.

Suggestions for Activity 2

1   You need to work out

(2 × 20) + (2 × 40)

= 40 + 80

= 120 m.

2   You need to work out

(2 × 10) + (2 × 13)

= 20 + 26 m

= 46 m.

Summary

In this topic you have learned how to measure or work out the perimeter of a shape.

> Topic 1 helps you cover this part of the Common Measures curriculum:
>
> ● 'work out the perimeter of simple shapes'.

Curr. ref: MSS1/L1.9

Topic 2: Area

In this topic, you will learn how to work out the area of rectangular shapes. This will help you calculate how much carpet you need for a room, how much paint you need to cover a wall or how much paving you need for a patio.

This patio has paving slabs that are 1 metre square (each side is 1 metre). How many paving slabs are there on the patio?

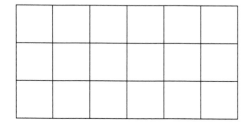

There are three rows of six squares. If you count them, you will find there are

6×3

= 18 squares.

Working with area

Area is the size of a surface. We measure area in 'square' units. This means that the area is shown as the number of squares of that unit that would cover the surface. In the example you've just worked on, the patio is covered with 18 squares that are 1 metre by 1 metre, so the area is 18 square metres.

Smaller areas are measured in square centimetres. Larger areas can be measured in square kilometres or square miles.

> **Hint**
> Always use the same units for both sides. If you need to, convert one side to the same units as the other side.

You can work out the area of a **rectangle** by multiplying the long side by the short side:

width × length = area.

The patio is

6 m × 3 m = 18 square metres

'Square metres' can also be written 'sq m' or 'm²'.

Example 3

How much backing fabric is needed for this rug?

3 m

90 cm

You need to work out the width times the length.

90 cm × 3 m = area

First, convert the width to metres so that both sides are in the same units

90 cm = 0.9 m

0.9 m × 3 m = area

= 2.7 square metres.

Now try these.

Activity 3

1   How much plastic sheeting do you need to cover this pond for the winter?

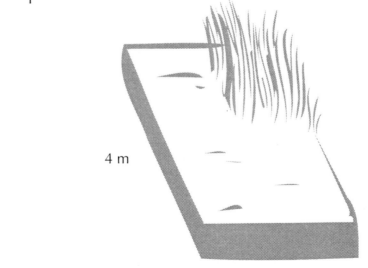

4 m

2.5 m

Activity 3 continued

2   One bag of gravel will cover half a square metre of ground. How many bags do you need to cover this driveway?

8 m

4 m

3   A biologist is studying yeast growth. In the sample area shown below the biologist found 80 yeast. Fill in the rest of the details on her recording sheet.

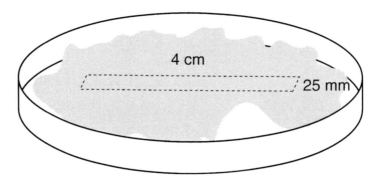

4 cm

25 mm

Yeast count

Sample area no.	*21*
Date	*17 October*
Yeast count	*80*
Sample dimensions	cm x cm
Sample area	cm²
Yeast/cm²	

Activity 3 continued

4   How large is this area of forestry land?

4.5 miles

2 miles

Look at our suggestions to check your answers.

Suggestions for Activity 3

1   You need to work out

2.5 × 4 = 10 square metres.

2   You need to work out the area of the driveway first:

8 × 4 = 32 square metres

Each bag will cover half a square metre, so you need two bags for each square metre:

32 × 2 = 64 bags.

3   You need to change the width to centimetres:

25 mm = 2.5 cm

Then work out the area:

2.5 × 4 = 10 square centimetres

There are 80 yeast, so

80 ÷ 10 = 8 yeast per cm^2

The sheet should look like this:

Yeast count	
Sample area no.	21
Date	17 October
Yeast count	80
Sample dimensions	2.5 cm x 4 cm
Sample area	10 cm^2
Yeast/cm^2	8

4   You need to work out

$4.5 \times 2 = 9$ square miles.

Summary

In this topic you have learned how to work out the area of a rectangular shape.

Topic 2 helps you cover this part of the Common Measures curriculum:

● 'work out the area of rectangles'.

Topic 3: Shapes with corners

Curr. ref: MSS1/L1.1

In this topic you will practise working with regular shapes. This will help you if you want to fit shapes together, perhaps to tile a floor or wall.

From where you are working, can you see any areas that are covered by shapes fitted together?

You might be able to see a tiled wall or floor, a paved area, or room dividers that are made up of rectangular panels. Perhaps there are ceiling panels – or you may be able to see some squared paper, or a cutting mat with guidelines in patterns.

Angles

Shapes with straight sides have corners where the sides meet.
A corner is an **angle** formed by two lines. Angles are measured in degrees, shown by this symbol: °.

A circle is a full turn. It has 360 degrees (360°). If we divide a circle into four you can see that there are four right-angles in the middle.

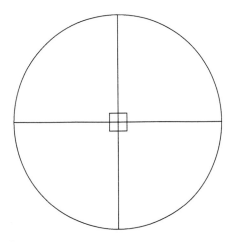

> **Hint**
> A right-angle can also be called a quarter turn.

Each **right-angle** is

$360 \div 4 = 90°$

A straight line is made up of two right-angles (180°):

Rectangles and squares have four right-angles. Added up, these come to 360°.

Some triangles have one right-angle.

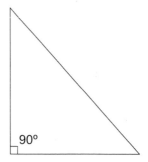

The angles in a triangle always add up to 180°. A triangle can't have two right-angles, as it would have nothing left for the third angle.

If you put two right-angled triangles together, they make a rectangle – with total angles of 360° (2 × 180 = 360).

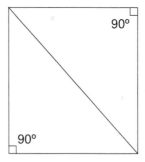

To cover an area without any gaps between shapes, you need every join to have a total of 360° when you add up all the angles.

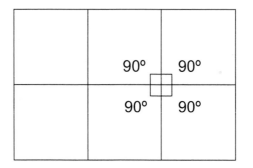

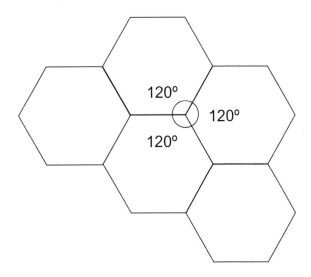

Number of sides shape has	Total angles
3 – triangle	180°
4 – rectangle, square, parallelogram	360°
5 – pentagon	540°
6 – hexagon	720°
8 – octagon	1080°

Example 4

A triangle has angles of 90° and 45°. What is the other angle?

Method:

The angles in a triangle add up to 180°, so you need to work out:

180 – (90 + 45)

= 180 – 135

= 45°.

Activity 4

What is the missing angle in each of these shapes?

a)

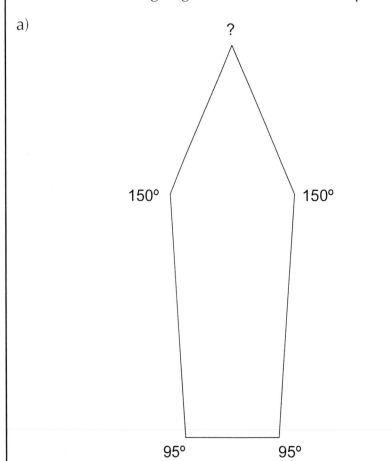

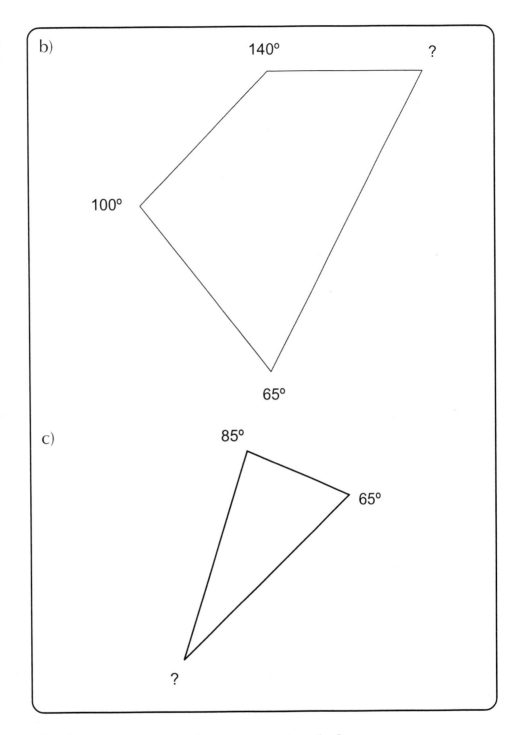

b)

140°   ?

100°

65°

c)

85°

65°

?

Check your answers with our suggestions before you move on.

Suggestions for Activity 4

a) The shape has five angles, so they must add up to 540°. You need to work out:

540 – (150 + 150 + 95 + 95)

= 540 – 490

= 50°.

b) The shape has four angles, so they must add up to 360°. You need to work out:

360 – (100 + 140 + 65)

= 360 – 305

= 55°.

c) The shape is a triangle, so the angles must add up to 180°. You need to work out:

180 – (85 + 65)

= 180 – 150

= 30°.

Making patterns

Some shapes fit together without leaving any gaps. These can be used to make a pattern on a surface. You need to fit shapes together if you are tiling or paving a surface or making a quilt.

Shapes that fit together without leaving any gaps are said to **tessellate**. A design of shapes fitted together is called a **tessellation**. Sometimes, the shapes have to be turned around to fit together properly.

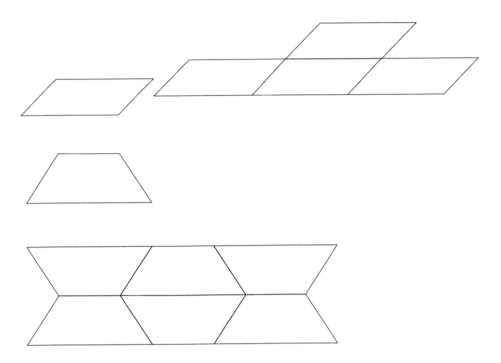

Many traditional designs for arts and crafts use patterns that are made from shapes fitted together. Islamic art and North American quilting patterns are two examples. Most of these use two or more shapes. Some are very complicated.

Here's a pattern made from octagons and squares.

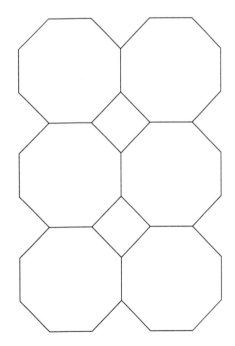

Example 5

Hint

Some patterns won't have neat edges. You might need to cut tiles in half to fill the gaps.

Tips

If you have to design a pattern like this, the easiest way is to cut out coloured squares and rectangles of card so that you can move them around to try out different arrangements. If you don't have coloured card or scissors, you can draw the pattern with a pencil and shade in one colour of tiles, leaving the others white.

You have to pave this area using a combination of tiles. Some tiles are square, 50 cm x 50 cm. Some tiles are rectangular, 50 cm x 100 cm. Design a regular pattern to cover the area. Here is a grid with squares of 50 cm to help you. Use one colour for the rectangular tiles and another for the square tiles.

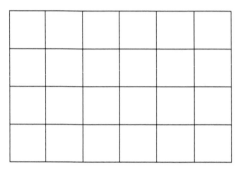

Method:

The rectangular tiles are twice as long as the square tiles, but the same width. There are several patterns you can make. Here is an example.

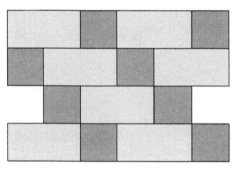

Now try these.

Activity 5

1 Design a pattern to be made up in two different colours of carpet tiles. All the tiles are square, and the same size.

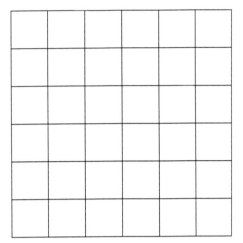

2 Which of these shapes could you use to make a pattern without leaving any gaps? Draw several of each shape on card and cut them out, then see if you can fit them together, or try drawing the shapes next to each other to make a repeating pattern with no gaps.

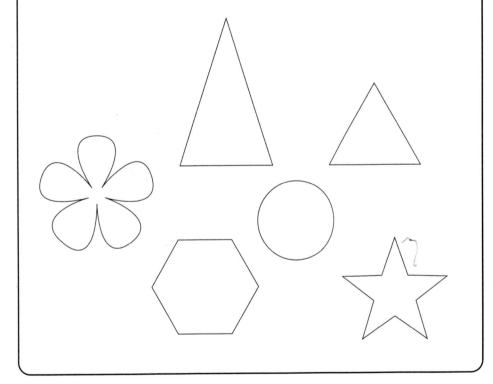

Check your answers with our suggestions before moving on.

Suggestions for Activity 5

1   There are lots of different designs you can make. Here are some
     suggestions.

2   You should have found that you could make a pattern with no
     gaps using the triangles or the hexagon (six-sided shape).

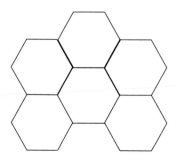 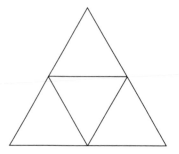

Summary

In this topic you have learned how to work with shapes that have angles.

> Topic 3 helps you cover this part of the Shape and Space curriculum:
>
> ● 'solve problems using the mathematical properties of regular 2-D shapes'.

Topic 4: Drawing plans and diagrams

Curr. ref: MSS1/L1.2

In this topic you will practise working with plans using simple shapes. This will help you to draw a plan of a room or other area.

Look around the room you are in. Which objects would look like rectangles or squares if seen from above?

Any of these could be square or rectangular from above: table, desk, washing machine, fridge, bench, rug, cupboard, filing cabinet, worktop.

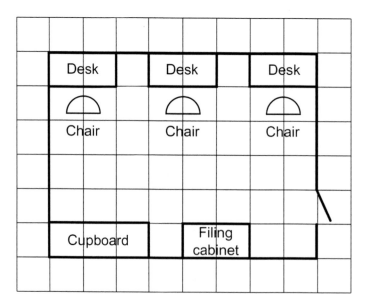

Plans

A **plan** shows a simple view from above of a room or another area, showing the things that are in it. Most plans are drawn to scale. This means that the size of an item on the plan relates to its size in the real world. For example, a room that is 3 m long might be shown as 30 cm long on a drawing. This uses a scale of

3 metres stands for 30 centimetres or

1 metre stands for 10 centimetres.

A table in the room that is 1 m long would be shown on the plan at 10 cm.

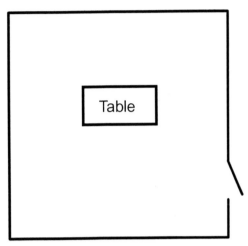

Scale 2 cm : 1 m

Drawing a scale plan is a useful way of working out how to arrange items in a space. You can use paper and pencil or the computer.

Example 6

You are planning a waiting area for a doctor's surgery. It will have six chairs, a coffee table and a water dispenser. The sizes of these items are:

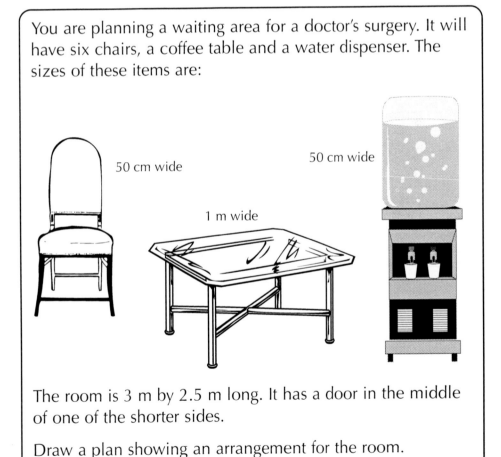

50 cm wide   1 m wide   50 cm wide

The room is 3 m by 2.5 m long. It has a door in the middle of one of the shorter sides.

Draw a plan showing an arrangement for the room.

Example 6 continued

Method:

Draw a scale outline of the room. We will use the scale 1 m = 2 cm.

Don't forget that the door will need to open, so you can't put any items directly behind it.

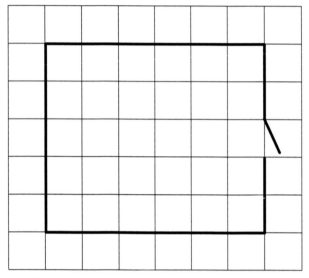

Scale 1 m : 2 cm

Draw a simple shape for each object, as though you are looking at it from the top.

Chairs

Table

Water Dispenser

Example 6 continued

Hints

If you have a pin board, you can pin the items in place. If not, you can use sticky-tack, or you can glue them down when you have decided your arrangement. If you don't have scissors, draw the shapes in place on your plan in pencil. You can rub them out if you change your mind.

If you can, cut out the shapes. You will need to cut out six copies of the chair.

Move the items around on the plan until you are happy with the arrangement.

You can turn the chairs around so that they face different ways.

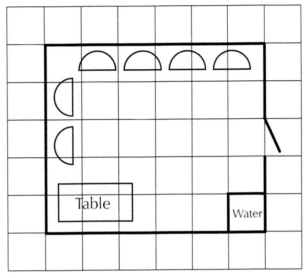

Scale 1 m = 2 cm

Now try these.

Activity 6

1   Draw a simple plan of the room you are in. Measure the room and the items you will put in your plan. Remember to convert the measurements to the same units before you start drawing. Use a scale of 1 m : 2 cm. (If the room is too big, you can stick more than one piece of paper together.)

**Activity 6
continued**

2   You have to plan a child's bedroom. Here is a plan of
     the space.

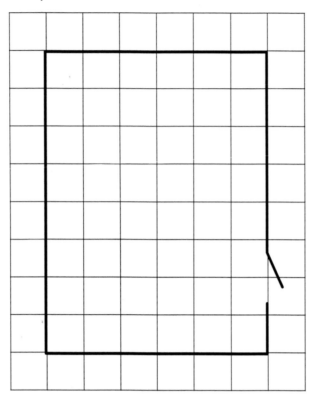

On a separate piece of paper, draw plan views of these
items that have to go in the room, using the same scale
as the room – 1 m = 2 cm.

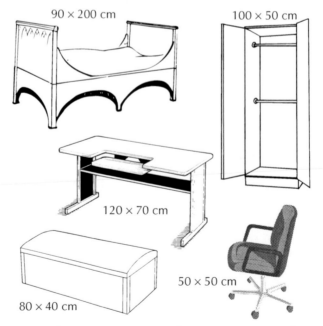

90 × 200 cm   100 × 50 cm

120 × 70 cm

80 × 40 cm   50 × 50 cm

Cut out your drawings. Move the items around on the
grid until you are happy with the arrangement.

Check your work against our suggestions before you move on.

Suggestions for Activity 6

1   This is what my room looks like:

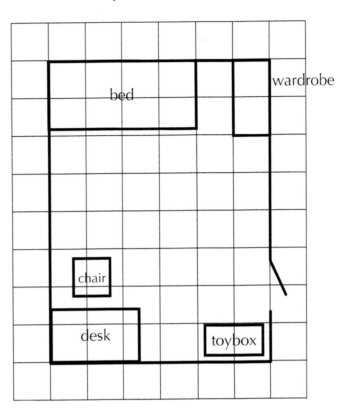

2   There are many ways you could have arranged the room. Here is one way:

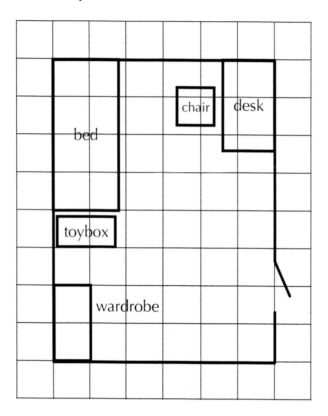

Summary

In this topic you have learned how to draw plans.

Topic 4 helps you cover this part of the Shape and Space curriculum:

● 'draw 2-D shapes'.

Section 5: Space

Section 5: Space

In this section you will practise working with the space occupied by three-dimensional shapes, or volumes.

Reasons for completing this section

Thinking about the things in this section will help you to:

- work out how much space a shape such as a box takes up

- work out how much something can contain – such as how much concrete is needed to fill a hole.

Topic 1: Volume

In this topic, you will find out how to work out the volume of a cuboid object. The volume of an object is a measure of how much space it takes up. If it is a hollow object, you can work out the volume it can contain. A **cuboid** is a rectangular or square box-shape.

Curr. ref: MSS1/L1.10

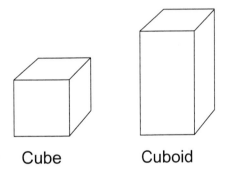

Cube   Cuboid

Can you see any cuboid items near you at the moment?

You might be able to see a box, a box file, a filing cabinet, a book, a cupboard, or perhaps a computer. Cuboids are lots of sizes.

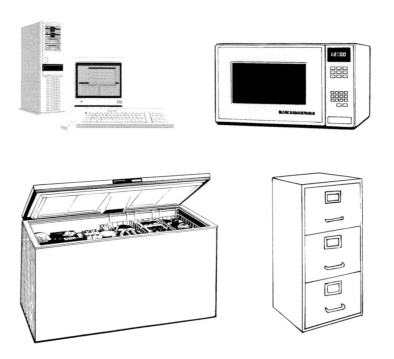

Thinking about volume

You might have seen a Rubik's Cube. It's a puzzle made up of small cubes fitted together into a large cube.

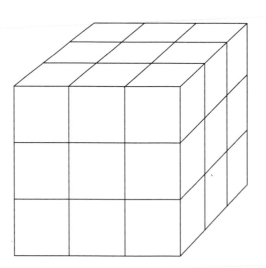

This Rubik's Cube has three cubes along each side. There is a total of 3 × 3 = 9 cubes in each face:

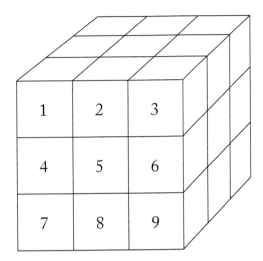

As there are three layers, there are $3 \times 9 = 27$ cubes all together.

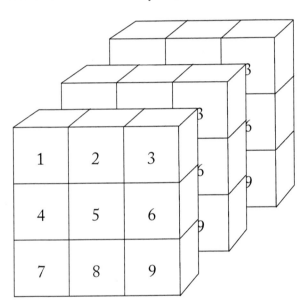

If each side of a small cube is 1 cm, each side of a big cube is 3 cm.

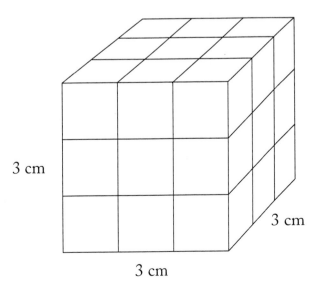

3 cm

3 cm

3 cm

The **area** of one face is 3 × 3 = 9 square centimetres (cm²).

The volume of the whole Rubik's cube is 3 × 9 = 27 cubic centimetres (cm³).

The volume of a cube or cuboid is

area × height.

As area is length × width, volume is equal to

length × width x height.

Volume is measured in '**cubic' units.** If you measure the sides in centimetres, the volume will be in cubic centimetres (cm³). If you measure the sides in metres, the volume will be in cubic metres (m³). If you measure the sides in yards, the volume will be in cubic yards (yd³).

In your work on capacity, you looked at litres and millilitres. A millilitre is the same as a cubic centimetre.

1,000 cubic centimetres = 1 litre

1,000 litres = 1 cubic metre

<table>
<tr><td>

Example 1

</td><td>

What is the volume of this box?

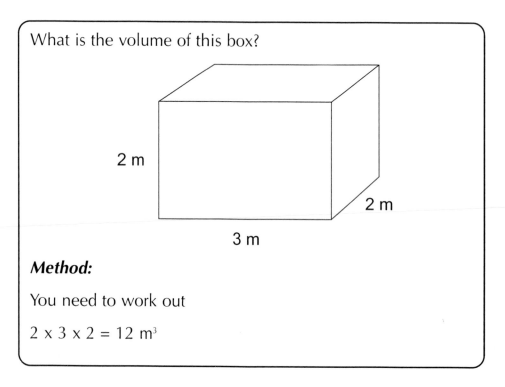

2 m

2 m

3 m

Method:

You need to work out

2 x 3 x 2 = 12 m³

</td></tr>
</table>

Now try these.

Activity 1

1   A builder needs to fill this hole with sand. He can order the sand in cubic metres. How many cubic metres does he need to order?

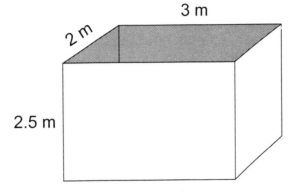

2   An aquarium has a new tank. There can be five fish for every cubic metre of water. How many fish can go in this tank?

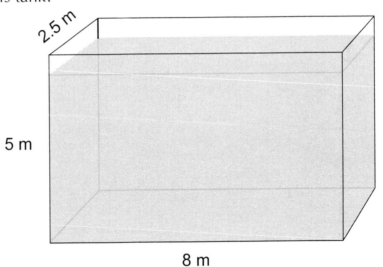

3   You have a window box that you want to fill with special soil for potted plants. How much soil do you need?

Hint

Convert the length of the long side to centimetres so that they are all in the same units.

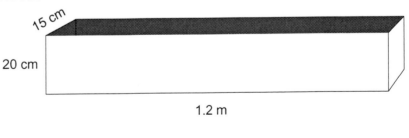

Check your answers with our suggestions before moving on.

Suggestions for Activity 1

1   You need to work out

$2.5 \times 2 \times 3 = 15$ cubic metres.

2   You need to work out the volume of the tank first:

$5 \times 8 \times 2.5 = 100$ cubic metres.

There can be five fish for each cubic metre:

$100 \times 5 = 500$ fish.

3   First, convert the length to the same units as the width and depth:

1.2 m = 120 cm

Then you need to work out

$120 \times 20 \times 15 = 36,000$ cubic centimetres.

Garden compost is often sold in bags labelled in litres. You would need 36 litres.

> **Hint**
> 1,000 cubic centimetres is 1 litre.

Summary

In this topic you have learned how to work out the volume of a cuboid.

> This topic helps you cover this part of the Common Measures curriculum:
>
> ● 'work out simple volumes'.

Glossary

Glossary

Al these words are used in 'Measures, shapes and space'. As they are key terms, they appear in the text in bold.

12-hour clock	clock that numbers the hours of the morning up to 12 and starts again for the hours of the afternoon. Morning times may be shown as 'am' and afternoon times as 'pm'
24-hour clock	clock that numbers the hours of the day up to 24. Times in the afternoon and evening are numbered 13–24
add up	to combine amounts to form a further quantity, called the sum
angle	corner made by two straight lines meeting
area	space occupied by a flat shape
breadth	how wide something is
capacity	volume (i.e. a measure of 3-D space), applied to liquids, materials that can be poured or containers
Celsius	metric measure of temperature in which water freezes at 0 degrees and boils at 100 degrees
centimetres	metric measure of distance; 100 centimetres = 1 metre
century	period of one hundred years
'cubic' units	units for measuring volume; a cubic inch is a cube with sides of one inch; a cubic centimetre is a cube with sides of one centimetre
cuboid	a solid shape with six sides, all or which are square or rectangular
distance	how far it is between two places

divide	split or share a number or quantity into equal portions; 8 divided by 2 splits 8 into two equal portions of 4
divisions	marks on a ruler, scales or other measuring instrument that correspond to units of measurement or fractions of a unit
estimate	make a thoughtful and careful guess by judging a distance, weight, etc or doing a rough calculation
Fahrenheit (degrees)	way of measuring temperature used before Celsius
grams	metric measure of weight
imperial units	system of measures used before metric measures; relations between units are based on numbers such as 8, 12, 14 and 16 – so 16 ounces = 1 pound, for instance
imperial weights	system of stones, pounds and ounces used to measure weight
kilograms	metric measure of weight: 1,000 grams
kilometres	metric measure of distance: 1,000 metres
litre	metric measure of volume
metres	metric measure of distance
metric units	system of measures first introduced by Napoleon Bonaparte that is based on multiples of 10, 100 and 1,000 – so 1,000 metres = 1 kilometre, for instance
metric weights	system of grams and kilograms used to measure weight
midday	12 noon
midnight	12 at night, when it becomes the next day
mileage chart	chart showing the distances between different places, measured in miles

miles	imperial measure of distance; 1 mile = 1,760 yards
millennium	period of 1,000 years
multiply	'times by': add a number to itself repeatedly, so '3 × 4' is three added together four times: '3 + 3 + 3 + 3'
perimeter	distance around the edge of a shape
plan	drawing that shows a flat view of an area, seen from above, and drawn as the outlines of the shapes
pounds	imperial measure of weight; 16 ounces = 1 pound
rectangle	shape with four straight sides with right-angles at each corner
right-angle	an angle of 90 degrees
scale	the relationship between a distance on a map or plan and the distance in the real world that the map or plan shows
stone	imperial measure of weight; 14 pounds = 1 stone
temperature	measure of heat
tessellate	repeat a shape to make a pattern
tessellation	pattern made by repeating a shape
thermometer	instrument for measuring temperature
time intervals	the amount of time that passes between two events or times
timetable	chart that shows the times at which an event takes place; a train timetable shows when trains leave and arrive at train stations
volume	the amount of space occupied by a solid or liquid

Information on the National Test

Information on the National Test

How is adult numeracy assessed?

To gain the certificate in Adult Numeracy at Level 1 you will need to pass a test covering all three modules in this course. The test lasts for one hour and 15 minutes. It is a multiple-choice test with 40 questions. This means that you will be given four possible answers to each question and you will have to pick the right answer. You will not have to write out any answers.

Entering for the test

You can take the test for the Certificate in Adult Numeracy at various times of the year. (Ask your nearest test centre for details and exact times.)

If you have been working through this series alone, you will need to contact a test centre to arrange to take the test. Your local college should be able to help you. If you need more help in finding a test centre you can phone **learndirect** on 0800 100 900. They will be able to give you details about centres near you.

Make sure you register for the test in plenty of time; some centres will need you to register two months before the test date. You may be charged a fee to take the test. You will need to ask the centre about this when you register.

Additional help to access assessment

If English is not your first language, or if you need help reading the test paper, you must tell the centre when you register for the test. You may be able to take a dictionary with you, or someone to help you read the paper.

If you need the centre to make any other arrangements so that you can take the test, you must talk to the centre when you register. The centre may need to check with other people about the arrangements or they may need time to make the arrangements.

Preparing for the test

- You need to complete all three workbooks in this series (*Handling Data*, *Number* and *Measures, Shape and Space*), or be confident in the skills covered, before taking the test.

- Make sure you know the date and the time of your test.

- Look back through the workbooks and the activities you have done.

- Try some multiple-choice tests. Ask the centre if they can provide you with any practice test papers. Alternatively, try the Key Skills example tests on the QCA website (www.qca.org.uk).

Taking a test can be scary but remember you have worked hard on the workbooks. The test is giving you the opportunity to prove how much you know.